Fat Matters

Other Health and Social Care books from M&K Publishing include:

Research Issues in Health and Social Care
ISBN: 978-1-905539-20-8 · 2009

Perspectives on Death and Dying
ISBN: 978-1-905539-21-5 · 2009

Identification and Treatment of Alcohol Dependency
ISBN: 978-1-905539-16-1 · 2008

Inter-professional Approaches to Young Fathers
ISBN: 978-1-905539-29-1 · 2008

The Clinician's Guide to Chronic Disease Management
for Long Term Conditions: A cognitive-behavioural approach
ISBN: 978-1-905539-15-4 · 2008

The ECG Workbook
ISBN: 978-1-905539-14-7 · 2008

Routine Blood Results Explained (2nd edition)
ISBN: 978-1-905539-38-3 · 2007

Improving Patient Outcomes
ISBN: 978-1-905539-06-2 · 2007

The Management of COPD in Primary and Secondary Care
ISBN: 978-1-905539-28-4 · 2007

Pre-Teen and Teenage Pregnancy:
A twenty-first century reality
ISBN: 978-1-905539-11-6 · 2007

Issues in Heart Failure Nursing
ISBN: 978-1-905539-00-0 · 2006

Fat Matters

From sociology to science

Gina Tsichlia
Alexandra Johnstone

Fat Matters: From sociology to science
Gina Tsichlia
Alexandra Johnstone

ISBN: 978-1-905539-39-0

First published 2010

British Library Catalogue in Publication Data
A catalogue record for this book is available from the British Library

Notice
Clinical practice and medical knowledge constantly evolve. Standard safety precautions must be followed, but, as knowledge is broadened by research, changes in practice, treatment and drug therapy may become necessary or appropriate. Readers must check the most current product information provided by the manufacturer of each drug to be administered and verify the dosages and correct administration, as well as contraindications. It is the responsibility of the practitioner, utilising the experience and knowledge of the patient, to determine dosages and the best treatment for each individual patient. Any brands mentioned in this book are as examples only and are not endorsed by the publisher. Neither the publisher nor the authors assume any liability for any injury and/or damage to persons or property arising from this publication.

To contact M&K Publishing write to:
M&K Update Ltd · The Old Bakery · St. John's Street
Keswick · Cumbria CA12 5AS
Tel: 01768 773030 · Fax: 01768 781099
publishing@mkupdate.co.uk
www.mkupdate.co.uk

Designed and typeset in 11pt Usherwood Book by Mary Blood
Printed in England by Reed's Printers, Penrith.

Contents

Figures

Tables

Contributors

Dr Sue Bird is the Knowledge Exchange Manager at the Rowett Research Institute, working with many end-users including policy makers, the general public, public health professionals and scientists. She has recently published 'Rational Food', a cross-curricular educational resource based on archive material from the Institute, tracing how rationing in World War II relates to current nutritional needs. Email: S.Bird@rowett.ac.uk

Professor John Blundell holds the Chair of Psychobiology in the Faculty of Medicine and Health at the University of Leeds in the UK, and holds professorial positions at the University of Liverpool and the University of Ghent in Belgium. He is currently chair of the Expert Group of ILSI (Europe) Task Force on Appetite Regulation, a member of the EASO Executive Committee and is actively involved in the Europe-wide Diogenes (Diet, Obesity and Genes) project. Email: J.E.Blundell@Leeds.ac.uk

Professor Iain Broom is Director of the Centre for Obesity Research and Epidemiology (CORE) based in the Institute for Health and Welfare Research, part of the Faculty of Health and Social Care at Robert Gordon University. He is also a Clinical Professor of Metabolic Medicine at the University of Aberdeen. He was, until his recent retirement from the NHS, a Consultant in Clinical Biochemistry and Metabolic Medicine within NHS Grampian. Iain also holds a Professorial Research Fellowship with the Rowett Research Institute. He sits on several national and European research committees as a member responsible for peer review of research activity and in a speciality advisory capacity. Email: j.broom@rgu.ac.uk

Dr Richard Butler is a Senior Lecturer and Director of Postgraduate Taught Programmes in the School of Engineering at the Robert Gordon University, Aberdeen. Since 1996, he has been active in research in the area of modelling metabolic systems. His work has focused on developing models, computer simulations, computer software and mobile software to empower people with diabetes to better understand and manage their condition. Email: r.a.butler@rgu.ac.uk

Dr Nuala Byrne is a Senior Lecturer at Queensland University of Technology in Brisbane, Australia. She is an exercise physiologist with interests in the role of exercise and dietary interventions in weight management. Email: byrne@qut.edu.au

Dr Rachel Colley is post-doctoral research fellow with the Healthy Active Living and Obesity Research Group (HALO) at the Children's Hospital of Eastern Ontario Research Institute in Ottawa, Canada. Her research is broadly focused on the role of physical activity in obesity and its related health complications. More specifically, she is aiming to further develop physical activity measurement techniques in order to characterise behavioural compensation responses to exercise interventions.
Email: rcolley@cheo.on.ca

Dr Diane T. Finegood is a professor in the Department of Biomedical Physiology and Kinesiology at Simon Fraser University, Burnaby, British Columbia, and she serves as the Executive Director of the CAPTURE Project, funded by the Canadian Partnership Against Cancer. She was the inaugural Scientific Director of the Canadian Institutes of Health Research, Institute of Nutrition, Metabolism and Diabetes (2000–2008). Her research interests include chronic disease systems, and modelling of obesity and body weight regulation in individuals and populations to identify novel solutions to the obesity problem.
Email: finegood@sfu.ca

Dr Allan Geliebter is a Senior Research Scientist in Psychiatry at Columbia University as well as a Professor of Psychology at Touro Graduate School of Education and Psychology, where he teaches courses in eating disorders, statistics, and research design. He is a licensed psychologist specialising in obesity and eating disorders. He has conducted a number of NIH-funded clinical trials to investigate BED and published numerous papers on pathophysiology and psychopathology in BED and obesity. Currently, he is the Principal Investigator of four NIH grants concerning binge eating and obesity. He has conducted various clinical trials and, most recently, conducted a double-blind multicentre drug trial with Rimonabant in obese binge eaters.
Email: ag58@columbia.edu

Professor Andrew Hills is Chair of the Energy Metabolism Group at Queensland University of Technology in Brisbane, Australia. His interest and expertise is associated with childhood obesity and exercise prescription for weight management.
Email: a.hills@qut.edu.au

Dr Alexandra M. Johnstone is a Senior Scientist within the Obesity and Metabolic Health Division at the Rowett Research Institute in Aberdeen. Her main areas of scientific interest are prevention and treatment of obesity and how dietary interventions impact on indices of energy balance, body composition, metabolism and health. More recent work has been on regulation of appetite with high-protein diets and how to improve insulin sensitivity by altering diet composition.
Email: a.johnstone@rowett.ac.uk

Dr Neil King is a Senior Lecturer at the Institute of Health and Biomedical Innovation, Queensland University of Technology, Brisbane, Australia. On a global level his research is involved with physical activity, diet and obesity. His research themes are individual variability and compensatory responses to physical activity interventions. Currently he is a co-investigator in a state-funded project in the UK titled 'Individual variability and characterisation of compensatory responses to exercise interventions'. The objective of the research is to identify and characterise individuals who may be resistant to physical activity-induced weight loss. The aim is to tailor physical activity and weight management strategies to suit individuals. He is involved in developing a mobile behavioural and physiological monitoring device to be used as a clinical research tool.
Email: n.king@qut.edu.au

Maria McQuigg is a Registered Dietician working within the NHS Grampian Healthcare Trust, Aberdeen. She has an interest in health promotion and health education and is currently working in training and supporting practice nurses, as a weight management adviser for the Counterweight project, on the delivery of a structured weight management programme in primary care to practices in Tayside and Grampian, under the auspices of the Scottish anticipatory care initiative, entitled *Keep Well*. Email: maria.mcquigg@counterweight.org

Dr. Christopher N. Ochner is an Assistant Professor of Clinical Psychology at the Columbia University College of Physicians and Surgeons. His research focuses on two main areas: environmental-approach obesity interventions and brain imaging of ingestive behavior. He has published several scholarly articles and book chapters, and delivered numerous invited lectures to international audiences. In addition, Dr Ochner has received several prestigious awards, and has been awarded independent grant funding from the National Institutes of Health and Columbia University, for his research on obesity.
Email: co2193@columbia.edu

Dr Sarah Pedersen is a Reader in Communication and Media at the Robert Gordon University, Aberdeen. She is the course leader of the MSc in Publishing Studies and Chair of the UK Association for Publishing Education. Her current research interests are focused on women's use of different media for support and validation in their daily lives. She is currently exploring women's use of blogs and parenting chatrooms. Her previous research investigated women's letters to the editor in Edwardian newspapers. Email: s.pedersen@rgu.ac.uk

Lauren M. Puma, MA, is a Clinical Psychology Ph.D. student in the Ferkauf Graduate School of Psychology at Yeshiva University, New York. She is also a research coordinator at the New York Obesity Research Centre at St Luke's Roosevelt Hospital. She heads the Post-Bariatric Surgery Cognitive Behavioural Therapy Program and bariatric surgery support groups at the Centre for Weight Loss Surgery located at St Luke's Hospital Medical Centre, New York. Her main research interests include obesity, bariatric surgery, and eating disorders. She has worked on several obesity-related grant studies, and has presented her research at international scientific conferences such as the Obesity Society, the Eating Disorders Research Society, and the Society for the Study of Ingestive Behaviour. As a mental health counsellor, her clinical work focuses on preparing gastric bypass and lap band patients for surgery using a cognitive behavioural approach.
Email: lmp2122@columbia.edu

Professor Matt Qvortrup is a Senior Research Fellow at University College London, and was formerly professor of Sociology at the Robert Gordon University. A former adviser to the British Government, he has written extensively in the areas of public policy, political theory and sociology. His research on the sociology of obesity was cited in the *New York Times* and by the BBC. Email: m.qvortrup@ucl.ac.uk

Dr Catherine Rolland is part of the Centre for Obesity Research and Epidemiology (CORE) based in the Institute for Health and Welfare Research, part of the Faculty of Health and Social Care at Robert Gordon University. She carried out her undergraduate degree at Queen's University in Kingston, Ontario, Canada, followed by an MSc and PhD at the University of Aberdeen, UK. Her current research interests include the effects of dietary interventions on obesity and associated comorbidities; adipokine responses to weight loss and dietary intake; and the use of proteomics in identifying novel proteins to clarify the mechanisms underlying obesity. Email: c.rolland@rgu.ac.uk

Dr Arthur D. Stewart is a Reader at the Robert Gordon University, Aberdeen. Dr Arthur Stewart has measured several thousand individuals using anthropometry, 3D scanning or other methods over the past 25 years. He holds the level 4 'Criterion Anthropometrist' qualification with the International Society for the Advancement of Kinanthropometry, and co-authored the ISAK manual in 2006. He is the kinanthropometry editor of the *Journal of Sports Sciences*, and regularly publishes his own research involving body composition and anthropometry. More recently his work has involved using 3D laser scanning to assess human physique in conjunction with weight loss and health risk.
Email: a.d.stewart@rgu.ac.uk

Gina Tsichlia is a Registered Dietician and Lecturer at the Robert Gordon University, Aberdeen. She is the Course Leader for the MSc in Sports Nutrition. Gina's research interests reside in the areas of obesity (psychopathology and sociology of the condition), sports nutrition and body composition. As a sports dietician, she has worked with Leeds United FC, Aston Villa FC and with individual professional athletes. Her doctoral research involves the refinement of a novel computerised method to assess body image in obese individuals. Email: g.tsichlia@rgu.ac.uk

Introduction

Obesity is never far away from the headlines. Every week we hear about a diet, a celebrity who has gained weight, or a new programme that promises to show us the way to a slimmer, sexier, younger, 'new edition' of ourselves. In a consumerist society obsessed with body image and thinness, obesity levels have reached an all-time high. With society currently in 'survival mode', trying to fight the consequences of the global economic meltdown and re-shape its lifestyle with changes as dramatic and painful as that of cosmetic surgery, will the recession affect our ever-expanding waistlines too? Or will it make some of us finally shrink to that dream of a size zero?

It is certainly time to start looking for some answers. This book will try to review, in a systematic way, different aspects of what has been referred to as the 'Obesity Epidemic'. We cover a range of issues from sociology through medicine to technology. This is not a book for the highly specialised expert. Rather it is a book that shows the diversity of approaches to the phenomenon of obesity, tailored to the reader who wants to be up-to-date and well-informed on a subject that is possibly as frequently discussed and as misunderstood as the weather.

In the first chapter, Sarah Pedersen explores our rather ambivalent attitude to fatness. She investigates how the media's celebration of a 'thin ideal' and its concomitant stigmatisation of those who are overweight or obese serve to hold a false mirror up to the realities of western society. Are there any interconnections between the media, body-image perceptions and obesity? Has our perspective changed over time? And how are the media shaping our consumerist society's slim aesthetic obsession to promote a false and unachievable body image?

In Chapter 2 Matt Qvortrup considers the social causes of obesity and why it seems that those in the lower echelons of society are more likely to be fat. He argues that this is not merely a result of diets but is also caused by working patterns in a global and deregulated society.

Arthur Stewart in Chapter 3 discusses the methodological problems of defining and measuring obesity. As he shows, this is more than a semantic and theoretical exercise – it has a real impact on those suffering from obesity.

The twent-first century is undoubtedly a time of great

technological advancements such as the mobile phone, personal digital assistants (PDAs), iPods and GPS systems. The obesity field could not escape a technological 'invasion' too. Although this is still a new field, software programs and even microchips have been successfully employed to tackle obesity, as Richard Butler argues in his chapter entitled 'The technology of obesity: Prevention and treatment'. The chapter raises the prospect that in the near future we might employ GPS systems to track our exact energy expenditure, analyse our exact daily dietary intake, acquire information about our energy peaks and lows and even get reminders on the screen of our mobile phone to 'have a snack' if our 'system' runs out of energy.

But, of course all this begs the question: what is obesity? Is there a single cause? Can we treat it and if so how? In Chapter 5 Iain Broom considers the clinical challenges in treating obese patients. He argues that one of the difficulties lies in the fact that Homo sapiens has – in some sense – become a new species and that this creates complications for the treatment of cases.

The Holy Grail of treating obesity is dieting. But – as most people who have been on a diet would probably admit – dieting is not a straightforward thing. Often diets are not as successful as the subject would have liked. Alexandra Johnstone and Sue Bird discuss this in their chapter, in which they explore the myths relating to diets and consider the fundamental question: Do diets work?

Sometimes in the quest to unfold the causes and find answers for obesity, it is easy to forget the individual. But obesity is not something that can be studied without taking the patients' perspectives into account. The subjective understanding of how it feels being obese is in many ways just as important as the objective analysis of the phenomenon. Anna Freud – the psychoanalyst and daughter of Sigmund Freud – is often (perhaps apocryphally) said to have defined empathy as 'the ability to step into someone else's shoes – and then step out again'. Whether correctly attributed or not, this definition encapsulates an important part of clinicians' training. It is therefore, interesting to read Diane Finegood's tale of her own battle with weight loss in Chapter 7.

Moving from the patient to perhaps the closest advocate in a patient's battle to lose weight, the dietician Maria McQuigg describes in Chapter 8 the issues raised by the current 'treatment' strategy within our National Health System and the impact it has on both the patient and the dietician as the 'diet expert' in the quest for weight loss.

Obesity is, in part, caused by inactivity. We are more sedentary than ever before. Throughout over 80,000 years of human evolution we have moved around. But we no longer chase after mammoths and boars like our ancestors. The environmental changes brought about by civilisation and the comfortable living that goes with it mean that we no longer burn as many calories as we used to as a species. This issue and its implications are analysed in King, Colley, Byrne, Hills and Blundell's Chapter 9, 'Physical inactivity, appetite regulation and obesity'.

Chapter 10, by Lauren Puma, Christopher Ochner and Allan Geliebter, deals with obesity as a psychological condition, another area that seems to have been overlooked in the literature. But obesity is not merely a physiological condition. It is not just about calorie intake and energy expenditure, it is also about how we feel about ourselves and about our bodies. As such, obesity is a psychological phenomenon – and one which can (in part) be treated as such.

We admit that this book covers a lot of ground. Not all readers will be interested in all chapters, but we are confident that we have comprehensively covered all aspects of obesity. Of course, there is much more research to be done in this area. But we hope that our endeavours can inform the public about this often discussed but little understood problem.

Gina Tsichlia
Aberdeen

Chapter 1
Female form in the media: Body image and obesity

Sarah Pedersen

The 'thin ideal'

Can we blame the media for the 'thin ideal'?

Many commentators suggest that the media's influence on body image stems from the 1920s when the illustrations in fashion magazines changed from drawings to photographs. Readers could now see, and aspire to look like, real fashion models wearing beautiful clothes or advertising expensive products. In the 1920s, magazines and the fashion industry taught that the ideal figure for a woman was a pre-adolescent one, with little or no bust or hips. This so-called 'flapper' figure showed off the new low-waisted dresses to their best advantage, and fashionable women took to binding their breasts, wearing restrictive corsets and dieting in order to achieve the look [1].

During the 1930s and 1940s a more mature female figure became the ideal, with the influence of film stars such as Jean Harlow and Mae West. However, clothes were still cut tight to the body, with an emphasis on the hips and bottom. The influence of Hollywood remained strong in the 1950s with icons such as Marilyn Monroe, with her hour-glass figure, setting the standard. The focus moved from hips to breasts, as exemplified by so-called 'sweater girls' such as Lana Turner. Such an emphasis on a 'womanly' figure came at the same time as women were being encouraged to return to domesticity and child-bearing after their involvement in the working life of World War II. However, by the end of the decade there was a move towards a slimmer figure, with actors such as Audrey Hepburn and Grace Kelly suggesting a connection between sophistication and slimness [2].

This renewed emphasis on a slim figure was taken to the extreme in the 1960s with the arrival of models such as Twiggy on the scene. The under-nourished and pre-adolescent 'waif' look dominated fashion magazines and the catwalks for the next two decades. However, this time there was a growing awareness of the costs of such an emphasis on thinness, and this combined with the Second Wave of the feminist movement to produce commentary such as Susie Orbach's *Fat is a Feminist Issue* published in 1978 and one of the first texts to explore women's attitudes to dieting and obesity. Orbach suggested that women stop dieting and start to explore the reasons why they were fat in the first place [3]. A growing awareness of eating disorders was further fuelled by the tragic death from anorexia of singer Karen Carpenter in 1983.

If you take a look at films or sitcoms from the 1970s, you will see slim figures, but not necessarily very toned ones. It was in the 1980s that the emphasis changed from one of slimness alone to the need for a tight, toned body, with exercise videos by celebrities such as Jane Fonda urging their viewers to 'feel the burn' and to achieve weight loss through exercise rather than just dieting. It was also in the 1980s that images of muscular and toned male bodies began to appear in the mainstream media, and commentators such as Grogan suggest that this increase in the visibility of the male body was paralleled by a growing preoccupation amongst men with their weight and body image [4].

The end of the twentieth century saw the rise of 'heroin chic', where fashion spreads in magazines used very thin models such as Kate Moss and made them up to look like drug users, with pallid skin and matted hair. However, renewed emphasis on a very thin ideal was this time accompanied by enormous attention to body image in the media. Newspapers, magazines and even specially convened government committees debated the damaging influence of pictures of super-thin models on young, impressionable girls. This debate has continued in recent years, addressing worrying trends such as size zero, the deaths of fashion models from anorexia and the rise of eating disorder support sites on the internet, where would-be anorexics can gain 'thinspiration' from photographs of very thin celebrities. Throughout this debate, the finger of blame has been pointed at the media itself. Critics suggest that the media has distorted western culture's idea of the female form by constantly promoting an extremely thin ideal, and that the media both reflects and moulds social pressure, on women in particular, to be a particular size and shape. Women's magazines are accused of using airbrushing and clever photography to produce an unattainable ideal and also mocking and humiliating those who have not achieved such an ideal by the use of cruel 'candid' photographs of celebrities' cellulite and weight gain.

Is it true that the media can influence people's attitudes towards their own bodies? The most dramatic example of such influence happened on the island of Fiji in the 1990s. In 1995 American television arrived on the island. Before this time, Fijian tradition admired and valued large female bodies as being symbolic of health and plenty and food was enjoyed without guilt. However, access to American television programmes such as *Beverley Hills 90210* introduced dieting and eating disorders to the island. By 1998 11per cent of women and girls on Fiji were engaged in self-induced vomiting, 29per cent were at risk of developing eating disorders, 69 per cent had dieted and 74 per cent admitted that they felt 'too fat'. Nothing else had changed on the island apart from access to Western cultural norms mediated through the television [5].

How are overweight and obese people represented in the media?

We have seen how the media is indicted by most commentators for the way in which it has shaped cultural expectations of body image. But how are overweight or obese people portrayed in the media themselves? In western culture, being overweight is often linked to laziness, a lack of will power or not being in control. Since the media both reflects and helps to form public opinion, it is not surprising to find this attitude to overweight people being reflected back at us in television programmes, magazines and films.

To begin with, there are far fewer overweight people shown on television shows or in magazines than there actually are in the real world. Take a look at the average prime-time television programme – the vast majority of characters will have an average or thin body. Greenberg and colleagues examined prime-time television series in the USA between 1999 and 2000. They suggest that thin women are particularly over-represented in such programmes. While around 5 per cent of women in the US are underweight, one-third of female TV characters have this body shape, as any viewer of *Sex and the City* or *Friends* will confirm. In

The role of the media

7

comparison, only 24 per cent of male and only 13 per cent of female characters are depicted as overweight, which under-represents the proportion of the population in the USA that is overweight or obese (30 per cent of men and 25 per cent of women) [6]. Fouts and Burggraf suggest that the figure is even lower for sitcoms with only 7 per cent of female characters and 13 per cent of male characters being above average weight [7].

Where a character is overweight, there may also be the implication that this says something about his or her character – that they are lazy or unable to control themselves. Such characters are rarely given major romantic storylines and overweight female characters in particular are frequently found in stereotypical submissive female roles such as nurses, cooks or housekeepers. For example, studies of prime-time television demonstrate that thin actors are given more major roles while overweight actors tend to be given supporting or minor roles [6]. Thus the media underlines the suggestion that success is related to being and staying slim.

This emphasis on thinness particularly impacts on women actors. Male actors such as Jack Nicholson or John Travolta can be seen to grow older and slightly more paunchy through the years and yet will still be offered film roles – and roles that still see them as sexually desirable. Women actors who allow themselves the same laxity find that the roles quickly dry up, a point made in the pseudo-reality television show *Fat Actress* starring Kirstie Alley.

While racist and sexist stereotypes have decreased in films and television programmes over the last twenty years, there is little evidence that the mocking of the overweight has diminished. In fact, a character's size is now one of the safer attributes to poke fun at. Overweight actors in films and sitcoms are more likely to be the butt of jokes, with overweight female characters in particular depicted as unattractive and disrespected by other characters. Overweight male characters also tend to be considered less attractive but are not as likely to be the butt of other characters' jokes about their weight. In fact, overweight male characters are more likely to make jokes about their weight themselves, perhaps teaching the overweight males in their audience that it is better to make a joke about yourself before others do it for you [8].

Researchers such as Himes and Thompson refer to such

characterisation as 'fat stigmatization' – the devaluing of an individual because of their excess body weight [9]. Their research into television programmes and films shows that comments about an overweight character's body and fat humour are often presented directly in front of the fat character themselves. In addition, they suggest that male characters are three times as likely as female characters to engage in such fat humour, demonstrating to their male audience that it is reasonable behaviour to make comments about a woman's weight and to judge that woman on the basis of her body shape.

Fouts and Burggraf found that in sitcoms the heavier the female character, the more negative comments were made about her and to her and that such comments were significantly reinforced by audience laughter. In addition, they found that the thinner the female character in sitcoms, the more positive comments she received about her body from male characters. Sitcoms are the most popular television programmes for young adolescents and so it is to this audience that the media promotes a state of permanent judgement and concern about physical appearance. Fouts and Burggraf point out that young female viewers learn from such programmes that men pay attention to female bodies and that if they fail to match the thin ideal they may be subject to derision and ridicule. In addition, those members of the television audience who are overweight and who identify with the heavier characters may be affected by such fat stigmatisation.

This is not to say that there are not successful overweight lead characters to be found on television. The comedians Roseanne Barr and Dawn French have had particularly successful careers for a number of years. Commentators such as Rowe have seen Barr in particular as an example of the 'unruly woman', demonstrating with both her body and her loud, rebellious behaviour, a transgression of society's rules for the way women are supposed to act. Both she and French 'make a spectacle' of their bodies, drawing attention to them and refusing to change or apologise for the amount of space they take up. In a culture that gauges femininity by how little space women take up, such actors insist on attention for their transgression of society's norms [10]. However, it should be noted that their weight is a very important part of both actors' characters, both on and off stage and that they are very much exceptions in their acceptance of and celebration of their size. As

Bordo points out, the norm is one in which the successful media star Oprah Winfrey has stated that the most significant achievement of her life – which has seen her become one of the most powerful women in media in the USA – was losing 67 lbs (30 kg) on a liquid diet [11].

On a more positive note, the limited amount of research that has focused on children's television programmes suggests a more positive and equitable picture is being presented here. Children's programmes do have some overweight characters but it is suggested that the proportion more closely reflects national figures (again the research was undertaken looking at American television). Children's sitcoms seemed to present their overweight characters as full members of the gang, less stereotyped than in adult programmes. However, overweight characters still suffer some social marginalisation and, while in the gang, are unlikely to be the leaders [12]. In addition, studies investigating children's animations have shown that children associate positive traits with thin and average-sized figures and negative traits with heavier ones.

Obesity in the news

**Obesity in
the news**

Research into the portrayal of obesity in the media has also investigated the way in which news programmes and newspapers frame the 'obesity problem' – the placing of blame for the growth of obesity in the Western world and the need for solutions. The mass media play an important role in the way any problem is defined to their audience, telling them what issues to think about and how to think about them. Kim and Willis suggest that over the last ten years, in both US newspapers and television news, mentions of personal causes and solutions have significantly outnumbered societal attributions of responsibility for the obesity problem, with TV news in particular more likely to mention personal solutions than newspapers [13]. They suggest the reasons for this are complex: the need for TV news programmes in particular to present individual news stories, usually focusing on a specific case, rather than placing the issue in a more abstract social context; the inherently political nature of any public health story; and the fact that the news media are simply reflecting mainstream opinion, portraying society as basically sound and attributing problems to corrupt or irresponsible individuals.

However, Kim and Willis point out that in recent years a decreasing number of personal solutions to obesity have appeared in newspapers, which have started to see the issue as a deeper-rooted societal problem requiring changes in society rather than just on the individual level.

Make me over

Finally, no discussion of how the media represents obesity can be complete without a mention of the 'make-over' show, which has become a staple of television schedules in the past few years. Such shows range from those that focus on clothes and how to wear them, such as *What Not to Wear*, to more extreme make-overs involving plastic surgery such as *Ten Years Younger*. One focus of all of these programmes is the participant's weight and how to disguise or 'slim down' her (and it usually is her) body, either by changing her personal style or by the use of restrictive underwear that will tuck her tummy, lift her boobs and minimise her bottom. Such programmes suggest to the audience that a new and 'better' woman, who will be more confident and successful in her daily life, will be the result. The emphasis throughout is on 'control' – the form-hugging underwear is usually referred to as 'control' pants, etc. Even a programme that claims to celebrate women's bodies in all their glory – *How to Look Good Naked* – ends up inserting them into control underwear in order to 'fit properly' into the chosen clothes. The message given to the participants and the viewers is that women have to control their bodies in order to conform to society's expectations of how they should look and behave. If they are able to control their unruly bodies and look as thin as possible, they will also be able to control their lives.

References

[1] Grogan, S. (2007). *Body Image: Understanding Body Dissatisfaction in Men, Women and Children*. 2nd edition. New York: Routledge.
[2] Mulvey, K. and Richards, M. (1998). *Decades of Beauty*. London: Hamlyn,
[3] Orbach, S. (1978). *Fat is a Feminist Issue*. New York and London: Paddington Press.
[4] Grogan, S. (2007). *Body Image: Understanding Body Dissatisfaction in Men, Women and Children*. 2nd edition. New York: Routledge.
[5] Becker, A.E., Burwell, R.A., Herzog, D.B., Hamburg, P. and Gilman, S.E. (2002). Eating behaviours and attitudes following prolonged exposure to

television among ethnic Fijian adolescent girls. *British Journal of Psychiatry* 180: 509–14.

[6] Greenberg, B.S., Eastin, M., Hofschire, L., Lachlan, K. and Brownell, K. (2003). Portrayals of overweight and obese individuals on commercial television. *American Journal of Public Health* 93 (8): 1342–8. Quoted in Himes, S. M. and Thompson, J. K. (2007) Fat stigmatization in television shows and movies: a content analysis. *Obesity* 15, 712–18.

[7] Fouts, G. and Burggraf, K. (2000). TV situation comedies: female weight, male negative comments, and audience reactions. *Sex Roles* 42 (9/10): 92532.

[8] Fouts, G. and Vaughan, K. (2002). Television sitcoms – male weight, negative references and audience reaction. *Sex Roles* 46 (11/12): 439–42.

[9] Himes, S.M. and Thompson, J.K. (2007). Fat stigmatization in television shows and movies: a content analysis. *Obesity* 15: 712–18.

[10] Rowe, K. (1996). Roseanne: unruly woman as domestic goddess. In Baehr, H. and Gray, A. (eds) *Turning it On: A reader in women and media*. London: Arnold, 81-86.

[11] Bordo, S. (1995). *Unbearable Weight: Feminism, Western Culture and the Body*. Berkeley: University of California Press, 60.

[12] Robinson, T., Callister, M. and Jankoski, T. (2008). Portrayal of body weight on children's television sitcoms: A content analysis. *Body Image* 5 (2): 141–51.

[13] Kim, S.H. and Willis, L.A. (2007). Talking about obesity: News framing of who is responsible for causing and fixing the problem. *Journal of Health Communication* 12 (4): 359–76.

Chapter 2
Social determinants of obesity
Matt Qvortrup

'Why are we so fat?' asked the American magazine *National Geographic* in a feature article in the summer of 2004 [1]. The use of the collective noun 'we' seemed particularly warranted as recent statistics show that more than 65 per cent of us (the British) are overweight (defined as having a body mass index of 25 or above). Still more alarming, 20 per cent of us are clinically obese (defined as having a body mass index of 30 or above). Britain is not alone in this. In America the figure is even higher; 30 per cent of Americans are obese. Fatness and thinness are issues of great concern in contemporary Britain (and, indeed, abroad). Body weight is a complex bio-psychosocial phenomenon shaped by many factors, including cultural, historical, and social character- istics [2]. All of these factors are important to consider in nutrition interventions and programmes. Below, I will outline some of the factors associated with obesity from a sociological perspective and draw on previous research [3].

Culture

The way we think about our bodies – and hence obesity – is shaped by our social context. Sociologists of health distinguish between the two words 'disease' and 'illness'. Where the former refers to objective symptoms (e.g. weight) the latter refers to the perception of the symptoms (e.g. how obesity is seen in society at large). The disease obesity – much like the disease anorexia nervosa – cannot be isolated from the illness obesity. Obesity is not only a medical condition, it is also a social construct [4]. Cultural values and norms about body weight vary considerably. Cross-cultural analyses suggest that most cultures in the world have valued moderate fatness and avoided extreme thinness [5]. In the 1960s Marilyn Monroe – a healthy size sixteen – was

Culture

considered the ideal. Today Kate Moss, size eight, is considered as a 'supermodel'. According to the Health Survey of England [6], the number of obese people grew by a stunning 400 per cent in the years between 1979 and 2004 (no similar study was carried out in Scotland). According to the same survey, 23 per cent of men were classified as obese. The figure for women was marginally higher at 25 per cent. Of course these measures are social constructs too. A medical definition is not – and cannot be – isolated from its cultural milieu. Yet the figure is alarming, not least because of the diseases which result from the Brits' failure to fight the flab. As the House of Commons Health Committee noted in its report: 'Should the gloomier scenarios relating to obesity turn out to be true, the sight of amputees will become much more familiar in the streets of Britain. There will be many more blind people. There will be a huge demand for kidney dialysis...this will be the first generation where children die before their parents as a consequence of childhood obesity' [7].

People in economically developed societies are more likely to be obese than those in developing societies [8]. As Ulrich Beck noted, the struggle for one's 'daily bread' has lost its urgency as a cardinal problem overshadowing everything else, compared to material subsistence in the first half of the twentieth century and to a third world menaced by hunger. For many people, problems of 'overweight' take the place of hunger [9]. Modernisation is the complex set of social changes that occur as societies shift from being 'traditional' to 'modern'. At the basic level, modernisation involves shifts in energy expenditure from muscle power to machine power, contributing to weight gain. Acculturation occurs as people become socialised into another culture. US studies suggest that acculturation into western society is associated with increased body weight [10].

Culture also shapes values, attitudes, and beliefs about fatness and thinness, providing a basis for how people interpret their own body weights and the weights of others. The dynamics of larger cultural changes and individual acculturation and migration reveal the overwhelming importance of culture in body weight and obesity.

Historical changes occur as societies move through time, and clear shifts have occurred in body weight and values about body size in many societies. Body weights increased in most societies of the world during the second half of the twentieth century [11], leading some observers to the conclusion that we are facing an obesity epidemic [12]. In Europe and America prior to 1900, plumpness was valued as insurance against consumptive illness. During the second half of the twentieth century, social ideals have increasingly emphasised the value of slimness for women. Social rejection of fatness has escalated since the beginning of the twentieth century. Historical patterns exist for body weight and attitudes about body weight and those patterns have been continually changing. It is essential to frame obesity within historical contexts to fully understand influences on fatness and thinness.

Social characteristics

Many social characteristics of individuals are associated with body weight in post-industrial societies. The social epidemiology of body weight can be examined in relation to twelve fundamental social characteristics of individuals that will be reviewed next.

Sex/gender

Biological sex differences in body fat, and social and psychological gender differences lead fatness and thinness to be female and feminist issues. Women are judged by and more concerned about physical appearance than men, with body weight and body shape being major criteria for judging female attractiveness. Stigmatisation of obese individuals is more prevalent and severe for women than men [13], leading to pressures that make body weight a 'normative discontent' for most women [14]. The prevalence and meaning of weight are vastly different for men and women, making weight a highly gendered issue. Little wonder, perhaps, that one of the most cited books in the emerging field is Susie Orbach's *Fat is a Feminist Issue*.

Age/Lifestage

Age refers to the chronological time since an individual's birth, and lifestage refers to the social roles and expectations that exist for people of a given age. In contemporary post-industrial societies, body weight and obesity tend to increase as a person ages, and then decline in the last decades of a person's life [15]. It is difficult to disentangle the relative contribution of biology versus social influences on patterns of weight by age. Activity levels of younger people tend to be higher, and decline as people age. Eating patterns also vary throughout the life course, influencing the caloric intake and body weight. Age and lifestage are consistently associated with body weight and obesity, with younger and older people being thinner and less likely to be obese.

Ethnicity

In the USA 44 per cent of all African American women weigh more than 120 per cent of their recommended body weight [16]. Of course such findings must be treated with due caution. Attribution of race/ethnic differences in body weight is extremely problematic. US ethnic variations in body weight tend to find most minority groups more likely to be obese than the majority. There is no consensus about the relative contribution of genetics, activity levels, or caloric intake to ethnic weight differences. Beliefs and attitudes about weight also differ among ethnic groups. Many US minority groups are more accepting of higher body weights than those in majority ethnic groups. Overall, ethnicity is a characteristic that is important to consider in relation to obesity, but it also presents complex questions about how and why it is associated with weight.

Employment

Employment involves work paid for by wages or salary in the labour force, either full-time or part-time. Some studies find that women who are not employed are more likely to be obese than their counterparts who participate in the labour force [17]. The same study suggests that unemployed men have been reported to be underweight. Even though the majority of adults in developed societies are employed outside the home, there is a dearth of information about how employment influences body weight. Mechanisms for activity level and caloric intake from employment are not well worked out.

Occupation

Occupation is the type of work that a person performs. Women in low prestige jobs tend to be more obese, but the relationship between occupation and weight is less consistent for men [18]. Energy intake is not necessarily determined by occupation, although some jobs provide eating opportunities that facilitate overeating and include obligations for employees to eat to perform their jobs, such as salespeople who take clients to meals, etc. Energy expenditure varies by occupation. Some jobs require employees to expend many calories over the course of their workday while other workers spend long sedentary hours on the job that can contribute to obesity. Occupations also vary in the flexibility they offer to workers to engage in recreational exercise. Overall, occupations provide lifestyles that play a role in eating, exercise, and weight management.

There is an inverse association between income and body weight in men and women in developed societies [19]. Income provides opportunities to exercise control over many aspects of life, including diet and activity levels. Overall, income is a powerful predictor of body weight levels and obesity. In post-industrial societies, higher income women in particular are thinner and less likely to be obese. Income provides many resources that permit people to avoid or overcome obesity, and is a component of patterns in obesity and interventions to prevent or reduce obesity.

Education

Perhaps not surprisingly, healthy eating is correlated with education. Education provides knowledge about eating, nutrition, activity, health and weight that is used in assessing food and activity choices and in managing body weight. Education also socialises people into the dominant norms of society about fatness and thinness, providing motivations and skills to conform to cultural weight expectations. Men and women with the least education tend to be heavier than their peers. Overall, education is one of the strongest predictors of body weight and obesity in populations, with more highly educated people being thinner [20]. The knowledge, thinking skills and normative socialisation acquired through education appear to be important in preventing weight gain during adulthood, and dealing with weight gains that do occur.

Household Size

Household size is related to eating patterns, activity levels, and body weight, particularly among some portions of the population such as the elderly. In particular, living alone is a risk factor for problematic eating, activity levels and body weight. Overall, the number of people with whom a person lives has the potential to influence their caloric intake, activity level, and values about body weight, especially for people living alone. However, relationships between household size and weight have not been a focus of past research.

Marriage

Marriage can be defined as the establishment of socially sanctioned marital relationships between men and women. Marriage is related to body weight and obesity in many different ways [21]. Obese people enter marriage later and marry heavier partners. Married men, but not necessarily women, weigh more than unmarried individuals. People tend to gain weight after entering marriage. People who terminate their marriages tend to lose weight. Overall, entering into marriage is more difficult for obese people, being married is associated with higher body weight, and terminating marriage is associated with weight loss.

Marriage structures people's lives, provides social obligations for eating and activities, and includes normative perceptions about body weight and shape. Marital status is a predictor of body weight levels, and effective interventions to change or maintain body weights can be structured around marital partners. Adult women cite having a child as one of the major reasons that they gained weight and are overweight. A small association exists between parity and weight, with an average gain of about 1 kilogram per child [22]. However, averages may be misleading because some women gain and retain considerable weight after childbirth while others lose weight, and the averages are modified by many sociodemographic and behavioural factors. Overall, being a parent is a significant role, and includes a myriad of dietary, activity, and other components that influence body weights.

Residential Density

Residential density refers to whether a person lives in a rural, suburban, or urban area. In the USA rural women are slightly more likely to be obese than their metropolitan counterparts. Rural residents have slightly higher caloric intakes [23]. While rural energy expenditure was traditionally high due to farmwork, the rise of mechanised farming and automobile transportation has decreased rural-urban differences. Attitudes and values in urban areas place more emphasis on thinness, leading people in cities to control their weight more actively.

Region

Region is the particular place where people live. Only scattered data exist about regional variations in obesity and body weight. In the USA, obesity is most concentrated in the South and Southeast. As the entire US population becomes fatter, obesity has spread to most regions of the country. Region appears to influence diet and activity, which in turn shapes body weight, but it is currently not clear why specific places have fatter or thinner populations, and more research on this topic is needed.

Conclusion

Obesity is a complex phenomenon. A subject that calls for more than biological research. 'Fatness' – a derogatory term – is a social phenomenon; an illness as much as a disease, to use the phraseology of medical sociology. Levels of obesity must be seen within their cultural and historical contexts, with each particular society and time period establishing broad conditions within which body weight levels occur for the population. In specific times and places, the social demographics of individuals are important influences on body weight patterns. Understanding social patterns is useful for those who deal with weight in their professional roles. Assessing and considering social factors helps to establish the social risks for obesity in individual clients or populations. Yet next to no research has been carried out in the field of sociology of obesity. At the moment findings comprise islands of knowledge without theoretical underpinnings, let alone clear strategies for how (sketchy) knowledge can be applied to meet policy targets.

When professionals decide whether to deal with body weight issues and which interventions to use, it is crucial to consider cultural, historical and social factors. Targeting changes to specific audiences also requires social patterns of body weight to be considered.

References

[1] *National Geographic Magazine*, August 2004.
http://ngm.nationalgeographic.com/ngm/0408/feature3
Accessed 12 December 2007.

[2] Sobal, J. (2001). Social and cultural influences on obesity. In Bjorntorp, P. (ed.), *International Textbook of Obesity*. London: John Wiley and Sons. pp. 305–22.

[3] Qvortrup, Matt (2005). Globalization and obesity. *Obesity in Practice* 1 (2): pp. 45–52.

[4] Turner, B.S. (1996). *Body and Society*. London: Sage.

[5] Anderson, J.L., Crawford, C.B., Nadeau, J. and Lindberg, T. (1992). Was the Dutchess of Windsor right? A cross-cultural review of the socioecology of ideals of female body shape. *Ethology and Sociobiology* 13:197–227.

[6] http://www.dh.gov.uk/en/Publicationsandstatistics/PublishedSurvey/Health SurveyForEngland/Healthsurveyresults/index.htm
(last accessed November 2009).

[7] House of Commons Health Committee (2003–04). *Obesity. Third Report Session. Volume I*. London: The Stationery Office.

[8] Sobal, J. (1999). Food system globalization, eating transformations, and nutrition transitions. In Grew, R. (ed) *Food in Global History*. Boulder, CO: Westview Press.

[9] Beck, U. (1997). *Risk Society: Towards a New Modernity*. London: Sage.

[10] Kylie Ball and Justin Kenardy (2002). Body weight, body image, and eating behaviours: Relationships with ethnicity and acculturation in a community sample of young Australian women, in *Eating Behaviors*, Vol 3, Issue 3, Autumn 2002, pp. 205–216

[11] Flegal, K.M., Carrol, M.D., Kuczmarski, R.J. and Johnson, C.L. (1998). Overweight and obesity trends in the United States: prevalence and trends, 1960–1994. *International Journal of Obesity* 22: 39–47.

[12] World Health Organization (1998). *Obesity – Preventing and managing a global epidemic*. Geneva: World Health Organization.

[13] Sobal, J. (1999). Sociological analysis of the stigmatisation of obesity. In Germov, J. and Williams, L. (eds) *A Sociology of Food and Nutrition: Introducing the Social Appetite*. Melbourne: Oxford University Press. pp. 187–204.

[14] Rodin, J., Silberstein, L. and Striegel-Moore, R. (1984). Women and weight: A normative discontent. In *Nebraska Symposium on Motivation*. Lincoln: University of Nebraska Press. pp. 267–303.

[15] Critser, G. (2003). *Fat Land: How Americans became the Fattest People in the World*. London: Allen Lane.

[16] Cossrow, N. and Falkner, B. (2004). Race/ethnic issues in obesity and obesity-related comorbidities. *Journal of Clinical Endocrinology & Metabolism* 89(6): 2590–4.

[17] Laitinen, J., Power, C., Ek, E., Sovio, U. and Järvelin, M.R. (2002). Unemployment and obesity among young adults in a northern Finland 1966 birth cohort. *Journal of Obesity* 26(10): 1329–38.

[18] Garcia, J. and Quintana-Domeque, C. (2006). Obesity, wages and employment in Europe.
Available at: http://ideas.repec.org/p/wpa/wuwpla/0508002.html
(last accessed November 2009).

[19] Cawley, J., Koyner, K. and Sobal, J. (2006). Size matters: The influence of adolescents' weight and height on dating and sex. *Rationality and Society* 18(1): 67–94.

[20] Lamerz, A., Kuepper-Nybelen, J., Wehle, C., Bruning, N., Trost-Brinkhues, G., Brenner, H., Hebebrand, J. and Herpertz-Dahlmann, B. (2005). Social class, parental education, and obesity prevalence in a study of six-year-old children in Germany. *International Journal of Obesity* 29: 373–80.

[21] Sobal, J. (1984). Marriage, obesity and dieting. *Marriage and Family Review* 7: 115–39.

[22] IOM-Institute of Medicine (1990). *Nutrition during Pregnancy: Weight Gain, Nutrient Supplements*. Washington, DC: National Academy Press.

[23] Tai-Seale, T., and Chandler, C. (2003). Nutrition and overweight concerns in rural areas: A literature review. Rural Healthy People 2010: A companion document to Healthy People 2010. Volume 2. College Station, TX: The Texas A&M University System Health Science Center, School of Rural Public Health, Southwest Rural Health Research Center. Available at:
http://www.srph.tamhsc.edu/centers/rhp2010/Vol2nutrition.htm
(last accessed November 2009).

Chapter 3
Assessing fatness

Arthur D. Stewart

This chapter seeks to address several key questions: What do we mean by fat, how do we measure it, and how can we use the knowledge of body composition? While these questions may appear straightforward, the answers are fraught with difficulties, which are often overlooked. We need a complete understanding of 'fatness' in order to avoid the confusion, which inevitably follows from different individuals and disciplines approaching the subject in different ways. One thing we can be very sure about is that fat gets a very bad press today. In bygone centuries, plumpness was a sign of wealth, but in the twenty-first century, the western world conditions us to believe that it is normal to be as skinny as Hollywood stars whose physiques are physiologically implausible for the vast majority of us. Fat is an essential ingredient of our bodies, as an electrical insulator for the nervous system, a physical shock absorber in the soles of the feet, a manufacturer of essential hormones and other chemicals, and a storage form of surplus energy.

What do we mean by 'fat'?

We can subdivide total body mass into its constituent parts by either anatomical or chemical methods. Under the anatomical model, total mass is the cumulative total of skeletal, muscle, adipose and residual tissues, as seen in Figure 3.1. This is the classical method by which anatomical dissections have identified body composition by weighing the component tissues [1]. The internal organs and the skin and associated integumentary structures are contained in the residual mass, which might typically account for about 25 per cent of total body mass. The skeletal mass includes all bones, cartilage and associated joint structures, and accounts for between 12 and 15 per cent of a typical adult's total mass. The other soft tissues are more variable, and muscle (mostly comprising water and protein) can account for as little as about 30 or as much as 65 per cent total body mass. Adipose tissue mass is even more variable, which can, in cases of severe undernourishment, fall below 2 per cent body mass, and in the case of the world's most obese person, exceed 80 per cent.

Figure 3.1   **An anatomical mass fractionation model**

(Adapted from Clarys, Martin and Drinkwater 1984)

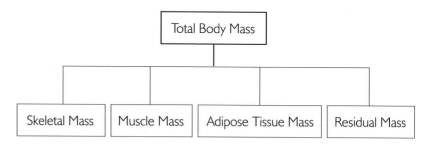

Under the chemical model, total mass is subdivided into fat mass and fat-free mass, which is further subdivided as seen in Figure 3.2. Fat mass is defined as 'ether-extractable lipid' and occupies between 80 and 90 per cent of adipose tissue. Crucially, the cell membranes, organelles, blood supply and intercellular fluid space form the non-fat component of adipose tissue. Because the size of fat cells (adipocytes) varies dramatically at different stages of the life cycle, and between different individuals (especially those of differing adiposity), the fat mass occupying adipose tissue (or the lipid-fraction) varies considerably. From here, the fat mass is further subdivided into essential, sex-specific and excess portions.

About 3–4 per cent of body mass is required to be fat in order to support the physiological processes which sustain life. In females, a further 7–12 per cent or thereabouts is necessary to support reproductive health, both in the capacity to manufacture sex hormones for fertility, and the energy requirement to make pregnancy a realistic physiological proposition. Above this, the excess fat accumulates in response to the energy balance of calories we consume and the cost of maintaining of lifestyles. A healthy 70 kg adult male may have 3 kg of essential fat and about 9 kg of excess fat, which would provide sufficient energy to sustain life for about eight weeks.

This well-designed mechanism allowed early humans to thrive with an intermittent food supply, but such Stone Age adaptations serve us less well in the modern environment of plentiful food supply, and we (in the western world) store reserves for a famine which never arrives. At the other end of the spectrum, many females involved in elite sport are exceptionally lean and deplete sex-specific fat reserves in order to optimise performance. Although this can be done successfully on a temporary basis, failure to recognise the symptoms in the longer term can lead to development of what has become known as the 'female athlete triad' of disorders: amenorrhoea, eating disorder and osteoporosis.

Figure 3.2

A chemical model of mass fractionation

(Adapted from Hawes and Martin 2001)

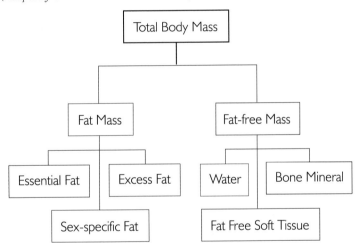

The fat-free mass (FFM) is subdivided into bone mineral (calcium hydroxyapatite), fat-free soft tissue (mostly tissues comprising proteins of various kinds and glycogen, the storage form of sugar) and water. The chemical groupings can be further subdivided from molecules into chemical elements, of which there are forty-four in the body. The disciplines collectively referred to as 'body composition' estimate the constituents of the body in different ways, using different assumptions, with different degrees of accuracy.

With this understanding clear in scientific terms, it becomes necessary to understand what the layperson considers fat to mean. Many concerned individuals dislike their perceived shape, and presume that this is due to fatness, while others weigh themselves on a daily basis, and over-interpret the natural fluctuations in their mass. What most individuals probably mean by 'How fat am I?' is 'what percentage of my total mass is fat?' but the question demands a comparator in order to convey meaning. This may be the opinion of a family member, a peer group, a supermodel, or even a body composition measurement in a weight management programme. Even if accurate, it is important to see the limitation of percentage values. Consider an 80 kg man who is 25 per cent fat. If he loses 10 kg (equally fat and fat-free soft tissue), his percentage fat would have dropped by only 3.6 per cent. In absolute terms, his fat mass has reduced by 5 kg. This introduces a dimension to estimating fat mass that is seldom appreciated. The composition of the weight gained or lost is always a composite of different tissues according to the models above, and not, as many would wish, entirely fat lost or muscle gained.

Methods of assessing fatness levels

Assessing fatness levels

This brings us to the next key question – 'How should we assess the level of fatness in a person?' Of the twenty or so different methods of doing this, it needs to be emphasised that all are approximations, and that only by anatomical dissection of a cadaver, and subsequent chemical analysis can the true composition be assessed. Every other method is an indirect prediction of the true value, based on a physical parameter of the living body. And because the body is living, such parameters exhibit biological fluctuations which frustrate the efforts of scientists to assess fatness accurately. Many methods are doubly indirect; that is, they predict what another prediction predicts, and although much more cost effective, have errors which relate to both methods.

At the most basic level, body mass includes all body tissues and so variability in mass cannot be attributed to fat, any more than other constituents, unless other measurements are made in addition. At the very least, weighing scales must be calibrated, checked and sited on a solid surface – and even with these caveats, comparison with results from a different scale may say more about the scale than the person being weighed. If stature is considered alongside mass, then it is possible to generate a score based on the relationship between the two, and common sense tells us that we would expect taller people to be heavier than shorter ones. Such indices include a simple height to weight ratio, the ponderal index (height divided by the cube root of mass) and the more common body mass index or BMI (mass divided by the square of height).

Body mass index

BMI was first considered by the Belgian astronomer Adolph Quetelet (1796–1874), who gave his name to the index, although he never specified that the square of height had to be used [2]. Since then the World Health Organization and many others have included BMI as a criterion for rating adiposity as shown in Figure 3.3. This may be logical for comparing populations, as height and weight can be easily measured in a census, but for individuals of different age, sex, ethnicity and body build, several difficulties arise.

Figure 3.3

The BMI scale used to rate underweight, overweight and obesity

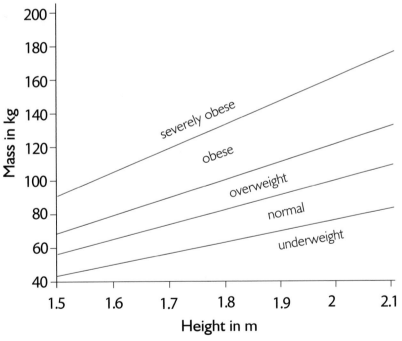

Convenient as the BMI is to calculate, it attributes excess mass to fat, whereas in reality, categorisation as overweight can be the result of muscular development, or a large frame size. In fact, the Western Samoans, who lead the world in BMI ratings, are unlikely to be the fattest, precisely because their natural body build is large-framed and muscular. Similarly, most international rugby forwards are mis-classified as obese due to their inherent muscularity. Females have less substantial skeletal structure and muscle development than males, and it is inappropriate to use a similar threshold to diagnose obesity for women and men using BMI, because the relationship between stature and mass is different [3]. However in western population terms, where fat people greatly outnumber muscular ones, the indiscriminate use of such a blunt instrument is not seen as a major problem, which goes some way to explaining the widespread use of BMI.

Beyond mass and height, other dimensional measurements can be made at the body surface via the science known as anthropometry. These measures include girths, lengths and skinfolds. Waist girth has been used as a surrogate for adiposity, and has considerable appeal as this can be done cheaply and conveniently, and does not require specialist equipment. Although the quality of tapes differ and some may stretch a little, producing measurement error, these are unlikely to contribute much to the overall error of measurement.

A far greater source of error is likely to be how the waist is actually measured. In a slim individual of an 'hourglass' shape the waist (usually defined as the narrowest circumference between the pelvis and the rib cage) is easily located. However, in a 'barrel shaped' subject, the waist cannot be located by this definition. 'Fixing' its position on an obese subject requires a standardised approach using anatomical landmarks, for instance 'at a level mid-way between the iliac crest and the thorax'. Using the midpoint of the navel is also done, though in very obese subjects with a pronounced panniculus (overhanging abdominal tissue) the navel is usually well below the pelvis. At the determined level, the tape should be maintained at right angles to the long axis of the upper body, which may not be quite horizontal because fatter subjects generally lean back in order to maintain balance. There should be no visible indentation of the skin, the tape should span the concavity of the back in a straight line, and measurements should be made at the end of a normal expiration.

Waist-to-hip ratio

Another frequently used index is the waist-to-hip ratio – a simple expression of waist girth divided by hip girth. Modesty generally prevents hip measures being made against the skin so, aside from the uncertainties of location, clothing can contribute to error if it is sufficiently thick. Even though this error is significant, there are issues of fat distribution which can see a large variation in fat quantity with little or no change in waist-to-hip ratio. This is problematic if the primary task is to diagnose a health risk, though the ratio can track individuals as they gain or lose weight. More recently, some clinical applications have used waist-to-stature ratio which is a more robust index, because it is reasonable to expect taller individuals to have a larger girth.

Skinfolds

None of the measurements mentioned hitherto have any direct value attributable to adipose tissue. Skinfolds, on the other hand, are raised double folds of adipose tissue, compressed by the skin caliper against a known closing pressure. These are located in standardised sites throughout the body which reflect the totality of adipose tissue distribution in places which can be located via anatomical landmarking – a systematic approach involving marking the skin surface to standardise its location against the underlying skeletal structure.

Skinfold measurements have been made since the 1920s to indicate relative fatness, and well over a hundred prediction equations relate the thickness of skinfolds to a fat mass or percentage fat. The main sources of error of the skinfolds themselves are the measurer, the location of landmarks, and the technique of measuring. For instance, the primary sites for measuring include the biceps and triceps of the upper arm, but the actual means of locating each site accurately is different. Location matters because the depth of adipose tissue varies markedly in some individuals with only a minor variation in measurement site, and either a lack of or inadequate detail describing the location or orientation of the body for measurement contributes to wide discrepancy. Standardising the location of measurements is therefore essential. The other 'given' is standardising caliper technique which requires considerable training and experience. The protocol and scheme of qualifications offered by the International Society for the Advancement of Kinanthropometry [4] provides one effective system of quality assuring the data, which could be worthless if such safeguards were not in place. Caliper manufacturer is also a source of variation, but a lesser one, if calibrated instruments are being used.

A major misconception with determining fat content from

skinfolds is that one equation is suitable for everybody. Because there are genetic distinctions in how different ethnic groups distribute fat, and how much they have, equations need to be population specific in order to be valid. A review of equations with details of the population group [5] thus provides the user with the knowledge of which equation might be suitable, although an increasing body of opinion suggests that skinfolds should be measured and kept as skinfolds as a measure of adiposity, avoiding the error of conversion into percentage fat.

In addition to these relatively simple methods there are a range of more technical measures, which we turn to now.

Bioelectric Impedance Analysis (BIA)

BIA machines are portable, inexpensive and need minimal training to operate. As the technology has improved, such devices are readily available over the counter in chemist stores and can be found in many GPs' surgeries and local gyms. More recently, devices combining body weight and composition have entered the domestic market, bringing an unprecedented level of measurement into the consumer's home. However, it is important to appreciate the limitations of BIA before the results it produces so conveniently are mis-interpreted. In order to see why this might happen, it is first necessary to understand what exactly BIA is measuring. BIA measures the opposition to electrical flow arising from resistance and capacitance. These vary according to the tissue composition and the cross sectional area through which the current is flowing, and the length separating the source and detection electrodes. Because body fluids are highly conductive and fat, being anhydrous, is not, fat-free mass (FFM) is estimated, after adjusting for height, and fat mass derived by subtracting FFM from total body mass. In practice, most devices use a constant frequency of 50 KHz and a current so miniscule that participants cannot feel it at all. The criterion BIA measures is impedance, which is calculated as follows:

$$\text{Impedance } (Z) = [(\text{resistance})^2 + (\text{capacitance})^2]^{0.5}$$

Many over-the-counter devices only measure resistance, and ignore capacitance, which, although much less than resistance at the commonly used frequencies, can introduce error. A far greater potential source of error is that these same devices usually require the operator to input the sex, age, height and weight of the participant, which are entered into the algorithm, which dutifully delivers the fat content. However, up to 85 per cent of the prediction is generated by the data keyed in and not the measured impedance, by virtue of the equation the device uses to generate the prediction. As with skinfold equations, BIA equations need to be validated against a criterion method such as Dual X-ray Absorptiometry (DXA) (see p. 34), and are therefore population-specific. The difficulty with some commercially available devices is that their equations are not declared, so the user will not know if the volunteer being measured is having a valid prediction or not. This 'black box' effect, where the result is delivered without the user being able to see the steps of the calculation process, affects other methods besides BIA, but due to the recent development and affordability of BIA, well-intentioned but unscientific users are putting too much confidence in the results they generate. Beyond the prediction equation itself, a range of other factors affect body conductivity [6] including hydration, posture, body temperature, ambient temperature, limb proportions and muscularity. Varying these will vary the prediction, generating bogus fat estimations. For a useful guide to equations both for anthropometry and BIA, refer to Heyward [7].

Underwater weighing (Densitometry)

Most body tissues are denser than water and sink, except adipose tissue, explaining why a person with a high fat mass is commonly observed to float more readily than someone with a more muscular build. This observation exemplifies the principles of densitometry, as observed by Archimedes (287–212 BC) and was the 'gold standard' body composition method until the 1970s.

Since
Density = Mass/Volume [Equation 1]
by rearrangement of terms
Volume = Mass/Density [Equation 2]

Densitometry divides the body fat-free mass (FFM) and fat mass (FM). Because fat is the only body constituent with a specific gravity of less than 1.0, its quantity can be estimated from underwater weight using several key assumptions. The density of FM is assumed to be a constant 0.90 g/ml and FFM a uniform density of 1.10 g/ml. Although fat varies little in density, the constituents of FFM vary in both density and proportion. For instance, Afro-Caribbeans and strength athletes have dense FFM, and osteoporotic subjects have less dense FFM. The measured density is converted to percentage fat by established equations, e.g. Siri 1956 [8]:

% fat = [(4.95/Density) – 4.5] x 100 [Equation 3]

Body gas pivotally affects measured underwater weight, so residual lung volume requires assessment by dilution of inert gases or oxygen (or prediction from age and stature). Total error for repeated measures using the same subject equates to about 2.8 per cent fat, once all the factors are considered. Considering the desire for accurate methods for determining fatness, it is perhaps not surprising that such a method is no longer considered acceptable as a reference method. From Equations 1 and 2 above, the volume of the body is equivalent to the mass of water displaced (the measured underwater weight subtracted from the mass in air) divided by the water density. From this volume is subtracted the residual volume of the lungs at maximal expiration, plus an allowance for air trapped in the gastro-intestinal tract. It follows that:

Volume = Ma - Mw/Dw - (RV + G) [Equation 4]

where:

      Ma = mass of the body in air (kg)
      Mw = Measured underwater weight (kg)
      Dw = density of water (g/ml)
      RV = residual volume (ml)
      G = estimated gas in the gut (usually 100 ml)

The body volume as measured above is then substituted into Equation 2, using the mass in air to calculate the body density, from which percentage fat can be calculated [9]. Underwater weighing is problematic for those who are not water confident or who fail to exhale completely. Common practice is to record at least five or more trials, which can itself be problematic. Despite the plethora of equations predicting percentage fat which use densitometry as a reference, the violated assumptions of the method are exposed by many studies. For instance, Adams *et al.* [10], investigated professional football players predicted to have -12% fat, despite having measurable superficial adipose tissue. Such individuals were strength trained Afro-Caribbeans whose FFM density greatly exceeded the assumed value as a result of genetic and training, induced effects and thus invalidated the prediction model.

Air displacement plethysmography (ADP)

The recent development of ADP via the 'BOD POD' system (Life Measurement systems, Concord, CA) is becoming established and has replaced a considerable number of underwater weighing facilities. Using a similar body composition model to densitometry, ADP assesses body volume and relates the resultant

Figure 3.4   **The BOD POD measurement of body composition**

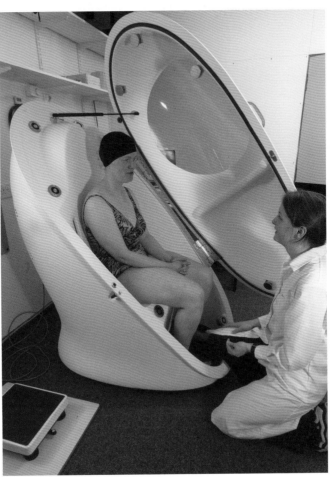

density to a percentage fat via a two-compartment model. The participant is seated inside a sealed chamber of known volume, linked via a movable diaphragm to a second chamber. The diaphragm is oscillated electronically, altering the volume of both chambers inside the capsule, inducing pressure changes which are dependent on the volume of the person in the first chamber. In practice, subjects wear a swim cap and swimwear. Various assumptions regarding the behaviour of gas under isothermal and adiabatic conditions are applied, and procedural compliance is scored in order to rate the acceptability of the measured thoracic volume. The main benefit of ADP over densitometry is the lack of requirement for subjects to be water-confident, although claustrophobia can deter some subjects from being comfortable inside the BOD POD capsule. ADP may supersede densitometry in the future. Further studies are needed to indicate a universal endorsement for replacing densitometry. Sensitivity to air movement within and beyond the measurement room can interfere with calibration, and locating the device in a suitable environment is essential.

Dual X-ray absorptiometry (DXA)

Dual energy X-ray absorptiometry (DXA) is a fairly new method for assessing body composition, originally developed for investigating bone. DXA involves X-ray beams of two energies passing through a subject. When they do, more of the weaker than the stronger beam is stopped by the absorbing material. How much of each beam is stopped by an absorber is referred to as attenuation, and the ratio of the attenuation at the two energies (the R value) is a measure of tissue composition, reflecting the atomic mass of the molecules and elements therein. While fat is principally carbon, hydrogen and oxygen, lean soft tissue contains several other elements – especially sodium, chlorine, potassium and phosphorus.

During a DXA scan, the participant lies on a scanning table above a source of X-rays. Strong and weak beams follow similar paths, and are detected by a moving arm above the subject. Further details on how DXA works are summarised in Pietrobelli *et al.* [11]. DXA makes a map of the R values of each part (pixel) of a scan area. Calculations are performed by automated software systems to discriminate bone from non-bone, and then to subdivide the non-bone pixels into fat and fat-free soft tissue. The end result is a regional map of the body detailing fat as well as bone mineral content (BMC) and fat-free soft tissue (FFST).

However, despite its relative sophistication, DXA has some limitations and its analysis requires several assumptions. DXA cannot 'see' behind a bone 'shadow', and must predict composition of soft tissue in the 40 per cent of the body map that contains bone. It does this by estimating composition from the composition of adjacent pixels with no bone. Sophisticated algorithms developed on real fat distribution in humans then input physiologically plausible values. This may be more sophisticated than it sounds because, as a cross-check, DXA has to arrive at a quantity of tissue completely independently of gravity, which corresponds to total body weight as measured on a scale. The fact that it can do this for a whole range of individuals of different size and fatness is a testimony to the effectiveness of the programming built in to the system software. R values depend both on tissue composition and tissue thickness, so the software will predict composition best for those in a normal range, but will be less accurate for extremes of size and fatness. Individuals taller than about 190 cm, heavier than about 140 kg, or with a body thickness more than 25 cm will produce less reliable results.

The DXA technology, developed in the late 1980s for assessing frail elderly women with osteoporosis, is now being used to measure healthy young adults, including athletes of different sports, and manufacturers have been slow to appreciate the requirement for larger scanning tables. X-rays can increase the relative risk of cancer, so life doses have to be carefully monitored via medical records to safeguard any individual. National or international guidelines governing the administration of radioactive substances require X-ray dosage to be minimised, although a DXA scan is a small fraction of the dose of a conventional chest X-ray (about one to two days background radiation, or the equivalent of one transatlantic flight). DXA provides a three-compartment fractionation of the body which has been shown to exceed that of densitometry alone [12]. Further, DXA quantifies both total and regional body composition with no subject discomfort (only lying supine for four minutes in one of the more recent array beam devices).

The disadvantages, aside from the radiation dosage, are the

loss of reliability in extremes of size and composition, and the fact that the three major suppliers of scanner use different X-ray voltages, pixel sizes and system software assumptions and generate results which are manufacturer-specific. In nutritional studies, knowing the fat content as accurately as possible is paramount, and a four-compartment method is generally accepted as the 'holy grail'. This uses densitometry or plethysmography to give fat mass and fat-free mass, which is further subdivided into bone mineral and water content by DXA and isotope dilution methods respectively.

Conclusion

For most of us, a surrogate measure of fatness is all we need to be confident that, while tracking change, the trend is up or down. All the methods have their limitations, many of which are little appreciated. But knowing their limitations and using the assessment methods appropriately is the key to unlocking their value.

References

[1] Clarys, J.P., Martin, A.D., and Drinkwater, D.T. (1984). Gross tissue weights in the human body by cadaver dissection. *Human Biology* 56: 459–73.

[2] Hawes, M.R. and Martin, A.D. (2001). Human body composition. In *Kinanthropometry and Exercise Physiology Laboratory Manual* (2nd Edition): Volume 1: *Anthropometry* (edited by R. Eston and T. Reilly), London: Routledge, pp. 7–46.

[3] Ross, W.D., Crawford, S.M., Kerr, D.A., Ward, R., Bailey, D.A. and Mirwald, R.M. (1988). Relationship of the body mass index with skinfolds, girths, and bone breadths in Canadian men and women aged 20–70 years. *American Journal of Physical Anthropology* 77: 169–73.

[4] Marfell-Jones, M., Olds, T., Stewart, A.D. and Carter, J.E.L. (2006). *International Standards for Anthropometric Assessment*. Potchesfstroom, South Africa: International Society for the Advancement of Kinanthropometry.

[5] Norton, K. (1996). Anthropometric estimation of body fat. In *Anthropometrica*, edited by K. Norton and T. Olds. Sydney: University of New South Wales Press.

[6] Baumgartner, R.N. (1996). Electrical impedance and total body electrical conductivity. In *Human Body Composition*, edited by A.R. Roche, S.B. Heymsfield, and T.G. Lohman. Champaign, IL: Human Kinetics.

[7] Heyward, V.H. (2004). *Applied Body Composition Assessment*, 2nd edition.

Champaign IL: Human Kinetics.

[8] Siri, W.E. (1956). *Advances in Biological and Medical Physics*, edited by J.H. Lawrence and C.A. Tobias. London & New York: Academic Press Inc.

[9] Kerr, D. and Stewart, A. (2008). Body composition in sport. In *Building a Champion Athlete: Applied Anatomy and Biomechanics in Sport*, edited by T. Ackland, B. Elliott and J. Bloomfield, pp. 67–86. Champaign, IL: Human Kinetics.

[10] Adams, J., Mottola, M., Bagnall, K.M. and McFadden, K.D. (1982). Total body fat content in a group of professional football players. *Canadian Journal of Applied Sport Science* 7: 36–40.

[11] Pietrobelli, A., Formica, C., Wang, Z. and Heymsfield, S. (1996). Dual-energy X-ray absorptiometry body composition model: review of physical concepts. *American Journal of Physiology* 271 (Endocrinol. Metab. 34), E 941–E951.

[12] Prior, B.M., Cureton, K.J., Modlesky, C.M., Evans, E.M., Sloniger, M.A., Saunders, M. and Lewis, R.D. (1997). In vivo validation of whole body composition estimates from dual-energy X-ray absorptiometry. *Journal of Applied Physiology* 83: 623–30.

Chapter 4

The technology of obesity: Prevention and treatment

Richard Butler

The past fifty years have seen a period of technological advancement unparalleled in human history. The pace of technological change in the fields of electronics, computing and communications and its impact on our everyday lives is breathtaking. We now take for granted technologies such as desktop computers, the internet, mobile phones, digital cameras and home blood glucose monitors for people with diabetes. But only a few decades ago these technologies were unheard of, or only in the realm of science fiction. Faced with the pace of technological change, even the informed can make predictions that underestimate the potential of technology. In 1949 the magazine *Popular Mechanics* contained an article that forecast future computers might perhaps only weigh 1.5 tonnes. In 1977 the President and founder of Digital Equipment Corp, Kenneth Olsen, commented that there was no reason for any individual to have a home computer.

This chapter presents a review of the human body as a metabolic machine and how this machine is fuelled. It also discusses the imbalance between the fuelling and activity of this machine and how this is leading to pandemics of obesity and Type 2 diabetes. The chapter continues with a review of the technology available to help people manage their energy balance – the difference between energy used and energy intake. The trends in this technology are reviewed and predictions made as to the future role of technology in the management of energy balance.

The metabolic machine

Our bodies are enormously complex metabolic machines. These 'body machines' and the mechanisms inside them have evolved over millennia to take their current form. Gowlett [1] presents a timeline for the evolution of man and of the diet of man. This is summarised in Table 4.1 (overleaf).

Table 4.1 **Fuelling the Metabolic Machine – from the Dawn of Humanity to the Present Day**

developed from Gowlett (2003)

Timeline	Evolutionary stage	Diet	Living environment	Evidence
10 million years ago	First traces of 'humanity' in the Great Apes – specifically chimpanzees	Fruit Meat Insects Honey Eggs	Rain forest	
8–10 million years ago	Hominids (human ancestors)	Addition of roots and tubers, less meat	Bush land	Teeth indicate more chewing, smaller canines
3–4 million years ago		More starchy carbohydrates	Savannah – seasonal environment	Teeth indicate heavier chewing
2 million years ago		Meat becomes more important	Temperate latitudes – meat eating more important – alternatives more limited	Stone tools, bones with cut marks
0.5–1.5 million years ago		Cooked meat, roots, tubers		Fire – saves energy costs in digestion, makes indigestible foods digestible
200,000 years ago	Ancestors of modern humans	Largely plant based	Tropical	
50,000 years ago		Mainly carnivorous diet	Arctic	
40,000 years ago	Modern humans enter Europe	Mainly meat based diet – maintained over hundreds of generations (30,000 years = 1,200 generations)		Cave paintings – very heavy representation of animals and hunting
10,000 years ago		Cereals arrive in diet Range of foods consumed reduces	Agriculture begins	
5,000 years ago		Dependency on milk and dairy products begins		

From the engineer's perspective, the machine has evolved to derive the fuel it needs to operate from a variety of sources – carbohydrates, fat and protein. The machine has the means by which the fuel can be stored in various forms – blood glucose, muscle glycogen, liver glycogen and fat. These stores have energy in readily available forms for near instant use, such as muscle glycogen, blood glucose and liver glycogen. Excess energy is converted to more efficient (but harder to access) means of storage for long-term storage, i.e. body fat. From the engineer's (and the machine's) perspective, the machine is operating as it was millennia ago. The pace of evolutionary change of the machine is very, very slow. The machine is still operating as it did as a hunter-gatherer in pre-history. There are short-term energy stores to provide pulses of energy for the chase – flight or fight. In times of plenty (i.e. summer) surplus energy is stored as fat for use in times of need (i.e. winter).

However, modern society has moved on from theculture of hunter-gatherers. Many people now live in a time of perpetual plenty. Unfortunately our metabolic machines have not evolved to cope with this change (and may not evolve to do so for many, many, millennia). The result is a pandemic of overweight and obese people in both the developed and developing world. The impact of this pandemic on the economy, health care and society is well documented in reports such as *Diabetes and Obesity: Time to ACT* [2]. A key question is what can the engineers and their technology do to help the metabolic machine cope with this relatively new world of plenty?

You are what you eat?

You are what you eat?

How do you know, when you eat and drink, how much fuel is being supplied for your metabolic machine? Is what you eat and drink providing your metabolic machine with the right types of fuel at the right times to meet your demands for energy and its demands to replenish its short-term energy stores of muscle glycogen and liver glycogen? Do you have fuel in the right places at the right times for what you want to do? Is your muscle glycogen store replenished ready for that next run? Is your liver glycogen store ready to help provide energy through the night while you sleep? These are key questions, particularly for people with diabetes. A current topic of debate is whether a return to the Palaeolithic, or

Stone Age, diet of our ancestors could be the answer to the modern day pandemics of obesity and Type 2 diabetes. Lindeberg et al.[3] concluded that a Palaeolithic diet based on lean meat, fish, vegetables and fruit may be effective in the prevention and treatment of common western diseases. Lindeberg advises that diary products, margarine, oils, refined sugar and cereals should be avoided and notes that these provide 70 per cent or more of the dietary intake in northern European populations. Lindeberg [4] comments on the current popularity in Sweden of a Palaeolithic diet, where lean meat, fish, vegetables, fruit, roots and nuts are dietary staples. In this diet, cereal, dairy products, salt and processed fat and sugar are avoided. Lindeberg comments that the digestive and metabolic systems of modern humans were not designed for dairy products, cereals, beans, refined fat, sugar, etc. These foods are relatively new features of the human diet. The human metabolism is still better suited to the Palaeolithic diet of primates and early humans. Lindeberg observes that it is not known whether Palaeolithic diets are more, or less, effective than other diets in weight reduction. Solomons [5] provided a review of the evolution of the human diet and its impact on chronic disease prevalence, and concludes that health systems need to change to address the twenty-first century pandemic of diet-induced chronic diseases, such as obesity and Type 2 diabetes.

In summary, Adams [6] may have been rather too close to the truth when he wrote, in humorous fiction, about humans having made a big mistake in coming down from the trees in the first place. Many believe that the root cause of people becoming overweight and obese is (as outlined above) the hunter-gatherer response of storing surplus fuel as body fat in anticipation of leaner times ahead. There is abundant advice available on diet and diet composition. Paper-based, software-based and online food databases are readily available and offer advice on the composition of foods in terms of macronutrients (protein, carbohydrates, sugars, fat and calories). How does this advice relate to meals and the metabolic machine? What will the pizza, chips and cola at lunchtime do for your metabolic machine? How much fuel is in this lunch? Will it help your machine to run smoothly or will the energy be in the wrong forms at the wrong times and be stored as body fat rather than used for activity or to replenish other energy stores? Is the fuel in the lunch in the right form, given the current state of the energy stores of the metabolic machine, for you to do what you want to do in the hours following this lunch? Will you have enough energy in the right stores at the right time? Do you really need all that fuel?

To answer these questions you would need to know:

(a) The state of the energy stores in your metabolic machine before lunch. Do any of the short-term stores (blood glucose, muscle glycogen, liver glycogen) need to be replenished? There is always energy in the body fat store, but it is difficult to access quickly. A good analogy is trying to buy a cup of coffee when all your money is in stocks and shares.

(b) The amount of fuel in the lunch and the form of this fuel. Lists of foods giving compositions in terms of macronutrients of carbohydrate, sugars, fat and protein abound in books and on websites. The UK government has recently introduced the 'traffic light' system of food labelling in an attempt to make the general public more aware of the composition of the foods they eat [7].

(c) How much of a food you consumed. Knowing the composition of say 100 grams of the food is one thing, but how many grams did you actually eat?

Engineers have developed technology such as compact, electronic weighing scales, accurate to grams for everyday use. Engineers have developed the computers and the internet to access databases of foods. Slimming and weight control websites that offer food composition databases are legion. There are food database software products available for personal computers and pocket computers.

What technologies are emerging and could emerge?

Emerging technologies

Technology, particular mobile technology platforms such as pocket computers, personal digital assistants (PDAs) and mobile phones, particularly smartphones, can feature food databases that can be accessed on the move. Personalised food databases have been developed that feature a personal selection of foods, personalised food portions and allow the building of a collection of foods into a selection of 'My Favourite Meals'. The Librae Body Double software, as described by Franklin [8], is an example of an application for a desktop or laptop computer that provides such a database. A PDA or mobile phone could be used to access and update a personalised food database, opening the possibility of using a mobile food model to establish how much fuel is in the pizza, chips and cola set out before you in a restaurant. A personalised metabolic model could be run on your mobile phone to allow you to visualise the impact of the pizza, chips and cola on your metabolic machine and its energy stores. Franklin's study, (mentioned above), of the use of the Librae Body Double software application for a desktop or laptop computer, concluded that for users to get full benefit, access to such software on a mobile device such as a phone or PDA was necessary. The need for technology to deliver solutions to provide e-health services has been recognised by health services, governments and the European Union. As part of the Sixth European Research Framework the European Commission has initiated projects (Information Communication Technologies for Health [9]) to investigate integrating different technologies in order to enable European citizens to choose healthier lifestyles. These feature small ubiquitous devices – such as mobile phones – to offer personalised advice.

What do you do?

What do you do?

How much fuel does your metabolic machine use each day? How much fuel do you need to play that game of tennis? How do you find out what you should eat to allow you to play and win that game of tennis? Without knowing this simple data, how can you possibly know how much fuel you need to take in through what you eat and drink?

Establishing the energy use of individuals in particular activities is notoriously difficult and relies on laboratory measurement of the individual in controlled circumstances, such as running on a treadmill with a plethora of instrumentation attached. The results of such work are difficult to translate to other individuals and other activities. Generalisations about how much energy a typical metabolic machine needs are available. For instance, the World Health Organization [10] has published a report on human energy requirements. These are based on a Basal Metabolic Rate (BMR) determined from the gender, age and weight of the individual. These BMR values are multiplied by a

Physical Activity Level (PAL) based on the individual's lifestyle. This combination of BMR and PAL can yield a number of calories per day required by the individual's metabolic machine. For specific activity (such as a game of tennis) specific Physical Activity Ratios (PAR) have been determined by experimentation with populations of individuals. The product of BMR, PAL and the duration of activity gives the calories required for the average individual (in the sample population) to perform that activity for that duration of time. An individual can determine their BMR and use appropriate PAL and PAR values to determine their typical daily energy expenditure and their expenditure in particular activities. This process involves an approximation to the BMR value and an estimate of the PAL or PAR values to be used. However, the outcome is unlikely to be accurate, and may be biased by the individual's view of their PAL or PAR values.

There is no substitute for recording what the activity (and fuel use) of the individual person is. The tricky part is how to do this. Low cost pedometers, that measure strides taken and give a result, do not yield a useful or accurate result in terms of fuel use. For instance, De Cocker et al. [11] studied the validity of data captured by low cost 'stepping meters' for 973 meters used by thirty-five volunteers over six days against activity data logged by an (accurate, but expensive) digiwalker device. They concluded that 'Inexpensive stepping meters cannot be used in community interventions as they will give participants the wrong message'(p. 714). Heart rate monitors as worn, or used, in gyms are a better way of recording the change in metabolic rate during exercise and this can then be related to fuel use. Accelerometers linked to data loggers give an indication of activity level, but are vulnerable to sources of acceleration other than the individual causing the movement. An evaluation of the accuracy of a low cost accelerometer based activity logger to a proven, expensive, activity data logger is presented by Godfrey et al. [12]. The evaluation involved ten healthy adults, the accuracy of activity log between their activePAL device and the proven data logger was found to be 98 per cent.

There are difficulties in using separate devices such as pedometers, heart rate monitors, accelerometers, etc. Firstly the user has to want to use the devices and remember to wear them. Secondly the device may be restrictive and prevent the user from wearing certain types of clothes or performing certain activities, such as swimming.

Health wear

Health wear

No single sensor technology can give enough information to accurately characterise fuel use. An array of different types of sensor is required to do this. This does introduce difficulties in terms of the convenience of fitting and wearing the sensors. The solution may lie in the emerging technologies of wearable sensors and wearable computing. Sensors and computing can be built into clothing. A classic example being the 'Lifeshirt' Continuous Ambulatory Monitoring System http://www.vivometrics.com/. Heilmann and Porges [13] discuss the use and accuracy of the Lifeshirt device in the detection of cardiac rhythms. The device was found to produce similar summary indices of heart rate and heart rate variability when compared to established monitoring techniques.

Sensing for life

Sensing for life

The need for an individual to wear sensors as separate devices or in garments is completely removed if the sensors are implanted within the body. Technology has already transformed the lives of millions of individuals by means of implants such as heart pace-makers, artificial joints and prosthetic limbs. Technologies are emerging for more complex implanted devices, such as an artificial pancreas for people with diabetes [14]. This device includes an implanted blood glucose sensor, controller and insulin pump. The blood glucose sensor detects the increase in blood glucose as energy from digested food arrives in the blood. The controller determines how much insulin to deliver to facilitate the movement of this amount of blood glucose from the blood so that the energy it contains can be used by the metabolic machine.

In the classic sci-fi space opera, the ship's doctor reaches for a gadget, waves it around and declares 'they are all dead Jim' or words to that effect. Could technology deliver a means by which the status of a metabolism (and its fuel use) could be sensed remotely? The semiconductor manufacturer Intel has developed such a technology, termed wireless sensor networks [15]. This technology brings together low power consumption sensing, computing and communications components called MOTES.

These are small, battery-powered sensors that can acquire data and communicate it using radio, to a remote location. A collection of these MOTE devices can form their own self-organising, self-healing, network to allow communications between individual MOTE devices. This allows, for instance, more remote MOTEs to relay their data via nearer MOTES. Applications for this new technology are beginning to emerge. One application in development is a project called Code Blue [16]. Faced with a major accident, like a train crash, the emergency services can dramatically improve the outcome for casualties if they are treated within the 'golden' first hour. Triage at the scene is essential to this process. The Code Blue project proposes that if the casualties all had worn or implanted MOTE devices monitoring their metabolism the emergency teams could interrogate the MOTEs and rapidly ascertain the status of each casualty.

Conclusion

Engineers are already working on technologies that will transform health care for millions of people in the next few decades. These technologies will offer the potential for a new, better, lifestyle for people with chronic conditions such as obesity and diabetes who choose to use them. These technologies will also ignite a cultural, ethical and psychological debate about how much the health service and/or a government should be able to monitor about the lifestyles and health of individuals. The challenge for the engineers lies in the technology adoption life cycle, as described by Moore [17]. The technologies outlined in this chapter that will help fight the pandemic of obesity and Type 2 diabetes are best described as 'disruptive'. People need to choose to use the technology to make a difference. As Moore describes, there are always a few people, innovators and early adopters who will try a new piece of technology because it is new. These are a small minority. Moore defined a 'chasm' that technology has to cross if it is to reach mass everyday use by the early and late majority and finally the laggards. A classic example is the group of people who 'will never use a computer and don't know how to', but have antilock brakes and engine management systems in their cars. The technology, and its complexity, are hidden from the user, but provide real benefits to the user.

The technology has to be robust, easy to use and provide a benefit with little (or no) effort for the user. In other words, if there is an easier way to do something – people will choose that way. Therein lies a challenge for engineers in the twenty-first century. Whatever technological interventions arise to meet the pandemic of obesity and Type 2 diabetes they will need to become as pervasive, and yet as hidden, as the antilock brakes in a car.

References

[1] Gowlett, J.A.J. (2003). What Actually was the Stone Age Diet? *Journal of Nutritional & Environmental Medicine* **13** (3): 143–7.

[2] Joint International Diabetes Federation (IDF) and International Association for the Study of Obesity (IASO) (2004). *Diabetes and Obesity: Time to ACT.* http://www.iotf.org/diabetes.asp (last accessed 20 March 2008).

[3] Lindeberg, S., Cordain, L. and Eaton, B.S. (2003). Biological and clinical potential of a Palaeolithic diet. *Journal of Nutritional and Environmental Medicine* **13** (3): 149–60.

[4] Lindeberg, S. (2005). Palaeolithic diet ('stone age' diet). *Scandinavian Journal of Food & Nutrition* **49** (2): 75–7.

[5] Solomons, N.W. (2005). Nutritional dilemmas of long term health: Implications of evolution and aging for policies and food industry practices affecting chronic diseases. *Asia Pacific Journal of Clinical Nutrition* **14** (CD supplement): 1–9.

[6] Adams, D. (1979). *The Hitchhiker's Guide to the Galaxy*. London: Pan Books.

[7] Food Standards Agency (2007). http://www.eatwell.gov.uk/foodlabels/trafficlights/ (last accessed 20 March 2008).

[8] Franklin, V.L., Wilson, A.W., Butler, R.A. and Greene, S.A. (2006). A predictive tool for the self management of diabetes (Librae): Evaluation using a Continuous Glucose Monitoring System. *Diabetic Medicine* **23**: 21–5.

[9] Information Communication Technologies for Health (2004). http://cordis.europa.eu/ist/health/index.html (last accessed 20 March 2008).

[10] World Health Organization (2004). *Human Energy Requirements*. Report of a Joint FAO/WHO/UNU Expert Consultation. Food and Nutrition Technical Report Series.

[11] De Cocker, K., Cardon, G. and De Bourbeaudhuij, I. (2006). Validity of the inexpensive stepping meter in counting steps in free living conditions: a pilot study. *British Journal of Sports Medicine* **40**: 714–16.

[12] Godfrey, A., Culhane, K.M. and Lyons, G.M. (2006). Comparison of the performance of the ActivePALTM Professional Physical Activity Logger to a discrete accelerometer-based activity monitor. *Medical Engineering and Physics* **29** (8): 930–4.

[13] Heilman, K.J. and Porges, S.W. (2007). Accuracy of the Lifeshirt®

(Viometrics) in the detection of cardiac rhythms. *Biological Psychology* 75: 300–5.

[14] Medtronic MiniMed (2007). http://www.minimed.com/about/index.html (last accessed 20 March 2008).

[15] Intel (2008). http://www.intel.com/research/sensornets/index.htm (last accessed 20 March 2008).

[16] CodeBlue (2007). www.eecs.harvard.edu/ ∼ mdw/proj/codeblue (last accessed 20 March 2008).

[17] Moore, G.A. (2002). *Crossing the Chasm: Marketing and Selling High-Tech Products to Mainstream Customers*. New York: Harper Business.

Chapter 5
Homo Adipatus – a new species:
Weight Management, treatment and prevention
Iain Broom and Catherine Rolland

The current obesity epidemic, indeed pandemic, is a major public health problem affecting not only the developed nations but also developing countries as they become modern industrialised nations. Over the last thirty years the prevalence of obesity has increased from 6–8 per cent to almost 25 per cent in the UK [1]. There have always been obese individuals within populations over the centuries and indeed in the nineteenth century, in the UK, increasing abdominal girth was seen as a sign of affluence and certainly not frowned upon. Obesity is still seen as such in developing countries.

The earliest depiction of the obese phenotype is from Stone-Age sculptures. The existence of such sculptures clearly demonstrates both the social importance attached to such a phenotype and the survival advantage conferred in accumulating large fat stores. The 'Venus of Willendorf' is the most famous of these (http://en.wikipedia.org/wiki/venus_of_Willendorf) and this sculpture's abundance of body fat is thought to have been diet related (high fat) in association with a sedentary lifestyle of cave confinement during the glacial era.

This way of life is not that different from our current dietary consumption of convenience high-fat, high-sugar meals in association with our computer/software driven lifestyle. One might suggest, looking at the changing body shape over the last half century, that Homo sapiens has evolved into Homo Adipatus (Figure 5.1, overleaf) and a new species has been created. Species development however depends on genetic change and takes hundreds if not thousands of years. The obese phenotype has evolved over the last fifty years and now accounts for approximately 25 per cent of the UK population and 30 per cent of the population of the USA.

Figure 5.1 **Homo Adipatus: a new species?**
Adapted from *The Economist* 2003 [2]

Homo Sapiens   Homo Adipatus

6 million years ago   **50 years ago**

The dangers in the rising weight of the nation relate to the impact of obesity on health. Obesity impacts extensively on both morbidity and mortality statistics. Although in earlier times obesity was seen to have a survival advantage during periods of famine, it was also recognised as early as 400 BC to have concomitant health hazards: 'Sudden death is more common in those who are naturally fat than in the lean'; 'Corpulence is not only a disease in its own right but a harbinger of others' (Greek physician, Hippocrates, 400 BC).

Today obesity is seen as the major aetiological factor in the development of Type 2 diabetes mellitus and is second only to smoking as the primary cause of cancer. Obesity is an independent risk for cardiovascular disease and is associated with the development of hypertension and dyslipidaemia, thus adversely influencing cardiometabolic risk. In addition obesity is linked to musculo-skeletal pathology, mental health problems and increased risk of inflammatory/infectious disease.

Aetiology of obesity

Aetiology of obesity

Although there is a clear genetic tendency for obesity to occur in families this in no way explains the current explosion of obesity seen across the world in the last half century. It is thought, however, that 40 per cent of the causation of obesity can be attributed to genetics. There are a number of single gene defects that can give rise to the obese phenotype, e.g. leptin deficiency,

MC-4 receptor defects and Laurence, Moon-Biedle syndrome. Very few patients have such problems and single gene defects do not contribute to the current pandemic. Obesity tends to be a polygenic disorder in origin and the obese phenotype is closely linked to environmental interactions with our genetic inheritance. There are numerous factors involved in the evolution of the obese phenotype and these are outlined in Figure 5.2.

Figure 5.2

Factors involved in the creation of Homo Adipatus [3]

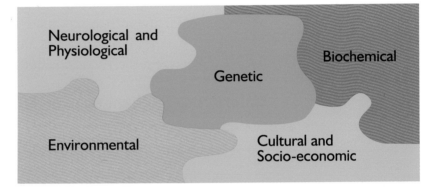

Clearly there have been no major gene changes in the world's population in the last fifty years and, since genes control our biochemical, neurological and physiological influences, it might be argued that these do not impact on the current pandemic either. We disagree. Obesity is a multifactorial condition where certain aspects (i.e. environment) can have repercussions on other aspects (i.e. genetic). These factors are all intertwined. Although the gene pool has not changed, other factors have an effect on susceptible genes. The factors influencing the development of the obese phenotype that have changed are a) environmental and b) cultural and socio-economic. It is the rapid change in these two areas that has impacted on our genetic inheritance to produce the obesity epidemic. Indeed obesity is probably the best example of a disease produced by altered gene–environment interactions. We have an inherited gene pool, moulded by famine over the millennia, that is ill-equipped to handle the current toxic obesogenic/diabetogenic environment. The environmental and cultural/socio-economic changes that have occurred in the last fifty years are huge, and Homo sapiens has not been able to adapt to such changes to allow energy homeostasis. Both the macro- and micro-environments of population and family have seen tremendous changes over this time period. Society operates completely differently in 2007 from the way it did in 1957. There have been major changes in demographics, alterations in transport, major increases in automation and differences in the way society perceives risk. All of these impact adversely on energy expenditure. Energy intake has also altered dramatically both in the nature of the food eaten and also in the mode of preparation and delivery. The impact of these changes is to affect a net positive energy balance in the individual with consequent deposition of fat and increasing weight.

Table 5.1 outlines the changes in adult energy expenditure in daily living between the 1950s and 2000s.

Table 5.1

Calorie usage changes over 50 years

Per week	1950s		2000s	
Shopping	On foot	2400	By car and supermarket	275
Washing clothes	By hand	1500	Washing machine	270
Making a coal fire		1300	Lighting a gas fire	3
Per hour	**1950s**		**2000s**	
Lawn mower	Manual	500	Electric mower	180
No power steering		96	With power steering	75

Figure 5.3

Schoolchildren involved in sporting activities (USA) Data from Centre for Disease Control 2000

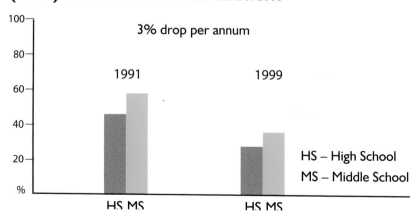

In 1980 there were 5,000 food items on supermarket shelves whereas in 2000 there were 35,000 food items. The increase in numbers relates, in the main, to pre-prepared and fast foods, which are often energy dense and appetite stimulating. Meals taken out of the home and snacking have increased dramatically over the years. All of these factors lead to a tendency to increased energy intake. Even the way food is eaten at home has changed, or rather the environment in which food is eaten has changed. No longer do families tend to sit round the table as a group to eat and to have social intercourse. This change in its own right leads to an increased rate of eating and hence increased consumption andalso tends to reduce energy expenditure on a daily basis by reducing small hand and face movements occurring during conversation. Societal changes in the shape of the 'free market economy', developed effectively in the 1980s, also impact on the level of obesity [4,5]. These external effects impact on a control mechanism for energy homeostasis that is molecular in nature and designed to cope with frequent episodes of famine and not with our current developed world's plenty.

Control of energy metabolism

Energy metabolism

The human body is designed to put weight on in periods of plentiful supply of food and to use these fat stores in periods of famine. Control mechanisms have evolved to allow survival of the species and hence to limit weight loss. Such processes are molecular in origin and involve cross-talk between the brain and the gut, and the brain and adipose tissue. These molecular mechanisms are extremely complex and are only just beginning to be unravelled. As the focus of these mechanisms is on preventing weight loss, it explains in part why achieving and maintaining weight loss in the overweight and obese is so difficult. The hypothalamus in the brain is the area organising the control of energy metabolism. This area could effectively be termed the body's thermostat. It receives and transmits messages from both the gut and adipose tissue and is responsible for responding in particular to energy deficits. Numerous protein molecules are involved in these mechanisms, both as receptors within the hypothalamus but also as proteins/peptides derived from both gut and adipose tissue. In brief, appetite signals and the need to eat to maintain body weight tend to derive from adipose tissue stores, whereas satiety signals are more relevant to gut-brain cross-talk. The relationships between these molecules and their complex cross-talk cannot be dealt with here in detail.

The major nutrients themselves have an effect on both appetite and satiety, as does the rate of food intake. Protein is the most satiating of the macronutrients, followed by carbohydrate, whereas fat in the diet has little effect on satiety or appetite. Hence a diet high in fat is likely to cause both increased food and energy intake.

(Discussions with respect to changing macronutrient content of the diet will be dealt with below in the treatment section.)

During periods of weight loss the hypothalamus swings into action to try and reduce the rate of weight loss by various mechanisms:

1) Switches from carbohydrate to fat as main energy source
2) Reduces the need to break down lean body mass to provide carbohydrate precursors for energy transduction
3) Reduces resting energy expenditure
4) Maintains 'thermostat' setting at the original body weight and correlates weight to adipose tissue stores, ensuring that the weight lost comes from adipose tissue – again to try to maintain lean body mass.

The overall effect is to limit weight loss and drive weight gain. Thus, during periods of weight loss, the hypothalamus is striving, by molecular means, to drive weight regain. Indeed even if weight loss ceases, this part of the brain will continue to drive weight upwards unless weight is maintained at the new reduced level for a considerable period of time.

Unless the reduced weight loss is maintained for some time, the hypothalamus (thermostat) will not reset at the new lower level, and the tendency will be for weight regain and indeed overshoot with eventual weight gain from baseline weight. This to some extent explains the natural history of obesity, i.e. to gain weight of approximately 1 to 2 kg per year despite intervening weight loss. It is now realised that adipose tissue is not just a storage depot for fat but is an endocrine organ in its own right, producing signal molecules to control not only energy metabolism but also immune functions and reproductive activity, and if allowed to accumulate in ectopic areas will increase risk of cardiometabolic disease. If accumulation of fat is increased, especially in ectopic areas, this produces a pro-inflammatory state, leading to exacerbation of inflammatory disease such as asthma and types of arthritis but also, by altering the redox potential of cells, fat accumulation has a pro-carcinogenic effect, leading to increased risk of neoplasia. Obesity, after cigarette smoking, is the second most common cause of cancer. Some of the protein signals produced by adipose tissue are outlined in Figure 5.4.

Figure 5.4   **Adipose tissue as an endocrine organ**

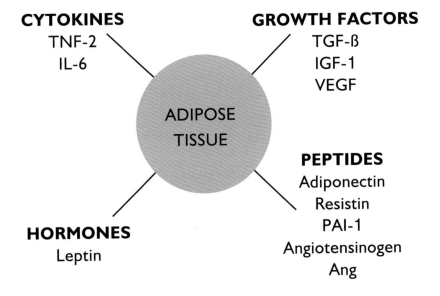

It is important to note that ectopic fat (such as viscera-associated fat) tends to produce more metabolically disadvantageous molecules, e.g. pro-inflammatory mediators. In addition such ectopic fat deposition tends to lead to reduction in adiponectin secretion, resulting in increased insulin resistance and increased CVD risk. Increased adipose tissue stores also tend to alter levels of sex steroid metabolism, leading to both fertility problems in females and males and increased risk of ovarian/breast/uterine cancer in females and prostate cancer in males. Overall our understanding of the complex control mechanisms in the obese state remains far from clear and further research in this area continues to be a major focus. There is also a clear need for future drug treatment in this area, with all major pharmaceutical firms supporting extensive research on energy regulation. This does not imply that drug treatment will be a panacea to deal with the current obesity pandemic, but it may help to control it.

Treatment strategies

Treatment strategies

Since the main focus of metabolic control is to prevent weight loss, treatment strategies for obesity management have proved extremely difficult for successive governments to agree on, both in the UK and elsewhere. The strategies currently in vogue are outlined in Table 5.2.

Table 5.2

Treatment strategies for the management of overweight and obesity

A. Governmental
- Lifestyle Modification
  - Dietary interventions ⎫
  - Increased activity ⎪
  - Decreased inactivity ⎬ Population and Individual
  - Behaviour modification ⎪
  - Stress management ⎭
- Drug Therapy
- Surgical Intervention
- Public Health/Health Promotion (to date ineffective)

B. Non-Governmental
- Patient-driven interventions with no evidence base
  - Herbal remedies
  - Fad diets

Lifestyle alteration remains the main focus of attention in managing the obesity epidemic. This effectively concentrates on three areas of intervention, with all the evidence suggesting that a combined approach using all three aspects is most effective. These include: dietary manipulation, increased activity/decreased inactivity and behaviour modification. It is clear from the literature that a combination of these approaches produces the best results in both the short and long term [6]. However, education of both patients and healthcare workers remains the prerequisite for successful management, as highlighted in the Counterweight Programme [7,8,9,10].

It is important to differentiate between population strategies and individual treatment programmes for the successful management of obesity, especially in the areas of diet and behaviour change; less so in the advocacy of increased activity. In relation to activity levels, it is essential that the population as a whole is encouraged to increase their activity levels and oppose their sedentary lifestyle encouraged by the ongoing environmental changes linked to automation and the sociopathic computer era. Individual increases in activity levels relating to reducing the obese state may have to be more tailored to specific individuals. It is not clear what particular form of increased activity is suited to a particular patient. Individual preferences may have to be taken into consideration. The countryside, open spaces and walking are free to all and reliance on 'exercise on prescription' is not a panacea. Motivational interviewing in this area, encouraging outdoor activities such as simple walking, will be much more effective and have no cost implications for the patient or government, local or national.

Dietary manipulation remains the mainstay of all obesity management programmes. As a population, the focus on reducing fats and sugar in the diet is appropriate and should be maintained. There is considerable evidence in support of high-fat, relatively low-carbohydrate (but high-sugar), low-fibre diets of western societies being a major aetiological factor in susceptible individuals. Excess dietary fat is more easily converted to adipose tissue lipid stores than carbohydrate [11]; diet-induced thermogenesis is less with fat than carbohydrates or protein. thus inducing lower metabolic rates with high-fat diets [12,13]; and dietary fat has minimal effects on both appetite and satiety [14]. Further education of both patients and healthcare staff in this area remains a priority [15]. Fast-food outlets, although tending to change their attitudes, remain a major barrier in this area, especially in relation to portion size. Thus high-fat diets lead to increased overall food consumption with marked energy intake, thus fuelling the obesity pandemic.

Focusing on a high-carbohydrate/low-fat diet is a sensible option for Government to adopt as far as population targets are concerned. On an individual basis however, this may not be the correct approach. It is essential when dealing with individual obese patients, to ascertain their habitual dietary intake. High-carbohydrate, low-fat intakes can also lead to obesity and individual advice may vary from that aimed at populations. Indeed the heaviest patients often have a problem with control of carbohydrate intake rather than fat. There is therefore room to consider the position of low-carbohydrate diets in the management of these individuals and taking an appropriate diet history is extremely important.

The role of very low-calorie diets (VLCDs) also needs to be reviewed. In some patients this may be important in achieving and maintaining weight loss. In the early 1970s and 1980s, such diets received much adverse publicity, due to their inappropriate constitution and consequent association with sudden death. Such problems arose out of inappropriate vitamin and trace metal content, resulting in cardiac dysrhythmias and death. Newer VLCDs do not have such problems and can be used safely in appropriate individuals. Commercial meal replacement programmes are also appropriate in the management of obesity at least in the short term [16,17]. More evidence is accumulating for their efficacy, although major clinical trials are sadly lacking.

Low glycaemic index diets are also in vogue and certainly are associated with a reduced insulin response compared with that seen with high glycaemic index diets. The reduced insulin response and the flatter blood glycaemic curve seen after food intake reduce the post-prandial appetite stimulation seen with carbohydrates that produce rapid glycaemic responses. Again major clinical trials in this area are lacking. The theoretical nature of this response is, however, appealing.

Behaviour therapy and associated stress management are also important in achieving long-term weight management. Cognitive behavioural therapy is the mainstay of behaviour change, in association with motivational interviewing. It is also important to be aware of the patient's 'readiness to change' before approaching behaviour alteration to achieve weight reduction.

Drug therapy is an important adjunct to lifestyle change in the management of obesity. It must, however, not be used in isolation but always in combination with the above lifestyle measures. Currently only three drugs are in use and recommended in Europe:

Orlistat – a lipase inhibitor

Sibutramine – a satiety enhancer

Rimonabant – an appetite suppressant.

All of these drugs in their clinical trials produced similar amounts of weight loss over their two-year period of trial, i.e. 5–10 per cent weight loss, and were superior to lifestyle modification alone.

Orlistat effects a net negative energy balance by inhibiting fat digestion and absorption in the gut. Approximately 30 per cent of the fat ingested is not absorbed and hence appears in the faeces. This drug thus acts as an antabuse to fat in the diet and ensures patients maintain a reduced fat intake. Failure to do so produces major gastro-intestinal side effects that will not be tolerated by patients, relatives and friends. Excess fat arriving in the large bowel is neutralised by gut bacteria, producing foul-smelling and colonic irritating molecules, resulting in explosive diarrhoea and excess flatus. This drug is therefore a useful adjunct where fat in the diet is the main contributor to obesity in that patient. If patients do not have a high fat intake and excess carbohydrate is the main contributing factor to the obese state, Orlistat is ineffective. Orlistat itself is not absorbed from the gut and is removed in the faeces, so there are no long-term or systemic effects associated with the drug. Both Sibutramine and Rimonabant act centrally on the brain in different areas of the hypothalamus.

Sibutramine is a satiety enhancer through its mechanism as a serotonin reuptake antagoniser. Serotonin is known to be involved in producing satiety signals in the hypothalamus. Sibutramine also acts peripherally as a nor-adrenaline reuptake inhibitor and can therefore, by increasing heart rate, lead to small increases in energy expenditure. There is also a risk of increasing blood pressure with this drug and careful monitoring is therefore necessary. Because of the effects on the sympathetic nervous system its use is contraindicated in patients with cardiovascular disease. As a result of possible drug interaction it is also contraindi-cated in patients receiving anti-depressant therapy.

Rimonabant acts centrally in the hypothalamus by blocking the endocannabinoid pathway. The endocannabinoid system, when stimulated, increases appetite, and is known to have increased activity in the obese. Rimonabant blocks the cannabinoid-1 receptor (CB1) in the hypothalamus, thus reducing appetite.

CB1 receptors are also present in other tissues, e.g. gut, adipose tissue, etc. By reducing the endocannabinoid tone periph-erally, Rimonabant also has a beneficial effect on insulin resistivity and serum cholesterol levels and is thus useful in patients with metabolic syndrome or Type 2 diabetes mellitus. Again because of its central action, especially in blocking 'pleasure pathways', it can markedly adversely affect mood. It is therefore not recommended for use in patients with a history of mood disorder. The use of drug therapy is restricted to patients with a BMI greater than 30 kg/m^2

or patients with a BMI greater than 28 kg/m² and with one or more associated comorbidities.

Surgery for obesity, bariatric surgery, has gained greater prominence over the years, as the obesity epidemic has spread. The development of minimally invasive techniques has also added to the increase in use of this approach to manage severe obesity. Indeed the primary treatment for patients with a BMI greater than 50 kg/m² is now that of bariatric surgery as indicated in NICE [18] guidelines for the management of obesity.

Bariatric surgery has two main approaches:
1. A restrictive procedure
2. A restrictive plus malabsorptive procedure.

Restrictive procedures reduce the capability of the individual to take large amounts of food by physically reducing the size of the stomach. This can be achieved by one of two methods: laparoscopic banding or a vertical banded gastroplasty (Figure 5.5).

Figure 5.5

Restrictive surgical procedure for managing obesity

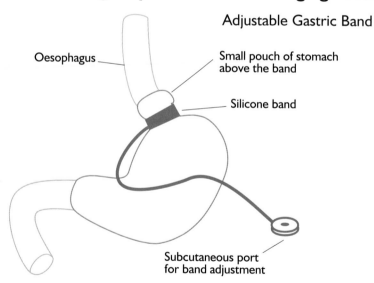

Both methods create a small gastric pouch with a narrow opening that restricts the emptying of solid food but allows normal emptying of liquids. Patients thus feel full after a relatively small meal and energy intake is thus drastically reduced. Both restrictive methods produce similar degrees of weight loss (~ 30 per cent of body weight in two years). Because of the lower complication rate associated with laparoscopic banding, this has become the restrictive procedure of choice. This procedure involves placing an encircling inflatable band around the upper part of the stomach, producing a small (15ml) gastric pouch. Post-operatively the band is progressively tightened, by introducing small volumes of fluid via an injection port inserted subcutaneously, until the appropriate degree of restriction is achieved to allow suitable weight loss. Such procedures are used in patients where the BMI is > 35 kg/m^2 with comorbidities or where the BMI is > 40 kg/m^2 without comorbidities.

In patients where the BMI is > 50 kg/m^2 restrictive/malabsorbtive procedures are more often employed. Again a small gastric pouch is created but in addition a varying degree of small intestinal bypass is produced, thus creating a malabsorptive process. The degree of bypass induced by surgery is somewhat dependent on the patient's BMI. Several different types of malabsorptive procedures are used; the most widely performed being the Roux en Y gastric bypass (Figure 5.6).

Figure 5.6

Roux en Y gastric bypass

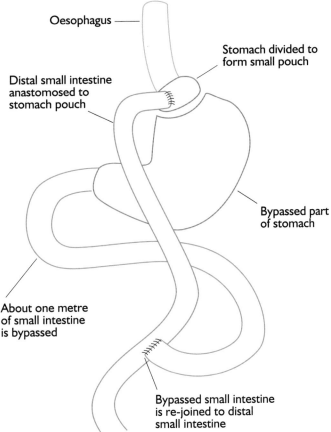

Oesophagus

Stomach divided to form small pouch

Distal small intestine anastomosed to stomach pouch

Bypassed part of stomach

About one metre of small intestine is bypassed

Bypassed small intestine is re-joined to distal small intestine

Food entering the gastric pouch exits through a limb of small bowel joined side to side to the pouch. The remainder of the stomach and first part of the intestine is bypassed, reducing absorptive capacity. There are other means of producing malabsorption of food using different surgical techniques, e.g. the biliopancreatic diversion and the duodenal switch, although these are not as commonly used as the Roux en Y procedure. Other treatments for the management of obesity include various herbal remedies and poorly constructed 'fad' diets. Neither of these have any evidence base with which to substantiate their claims. They are, however, frequently employed by the obese patient in an attempt to achieve and maintain weight loss. A great deal of commercial activity surrounds these claims, with resultant considerable but ineffective expense by the patients.

Conclusion

Despite numerous statements by government, and strategic attempts to achieve control of the population's weight, the obesity epidemic marches on. Because of the complex nature of the obesity epidemic, there is no easy solution to the problem. Environmental changes and alterations in socio-economic factors will continue to impact on our genetic inheritance and Homo Sapiens will need to learn to adapt to these changes if Homo Adipatus is to be avoided. This will require major fundamental input from all branches of government and not just from the Department of Health. Failure to halt the obesity epidemic, especially as it is now affecting our children, will see a return of children dying before their parents, a situation not uncommon in the nineteenth century and before, but rare in the latter part of the twentieth century. Much greater cooperation from the food industry than has hitherto been seen is required, as well as the cooperation of society as a whole, if the obesity epidemic is to be stopped and reversed.

References

[1] Thomas, P.R. (ed.) (1995). *Weighing the Options. Criteria for Evaluating Weight-Management Programs*. Washington, DC: National Academy Press.

[2] *The Economist* (2003). The world's expanding waistline. The shape of things to come. 11 December.

[3] Avenell, A., Broom, J., Brown, T.J., Poobalan, A., Aucott, L., Stearns, S.C., Smith, W.C.S., Jung, R.T., Campbell, M.K. and Grant, A.M. (2004). Systematic review of the long-term effects and economic consequences of treatments for obesity and implications for health improvement. *Health Technology Assessment NHS R&D HTA Programme* Vol. 8. No. 21.

[4] Baillie, K. (2008). Health implications of transition from a planned to a free-market economy – an overview. *Obesity Reviews* 9 (Suppl 1): 146–50.

[5] James, W.P.T. (2008). The epidemiology of obesity: the size of the problem. *Journal of Internal Medicine* 263: 336–52.

[6] Department of Health (2006). *Forecasting Obesity to 2010*. London: Crown.

[7] The Counterweight Project Team (2004). Current approaches to obesity management in UK primary care: the Counterweight Programme. *Journal of Human Nutrition and Dietetics* 17: 183–90.

[8] The Counterweight Project Team (2004). A new evidence-based model for weight management in primary care: the Counterweight Programme. *Journal of Human Nutrition and Dietetics* 17: 191–208.

[9] The Counterweight Project Team (2005). Empowering primary care to tackle the obesity epidemic: The Counterweight Programme. *European Journal of Clinical Nutrition* 59: Suppl. 1, S93–101.

[10] The Counterweight Project Team (2005). Obesity impacts on general practice appointments. *Obesity Research* 13 (8): 1442–9.

[11] Flatt, J.P. (1985). Energetics of intermediary metabolism. In *Substrate and Energy Metabolism*, eds. J.S. Garrow and D. Halliday. London: J. Libbey, pp. 58–69.

[12] Lean, M.E.J and James, W.P. (1988). Metabolic effects of isoenergetic nutrient exchange over 24 hours in relation to obesity in women. *International Journal of Obesity* 12: 15–27.

[13] Lean, M.E.J., James, W.P.T. and Garthwaite, P.H. (1989). Obesity without overeating? in *Obesity in Europe 88*, eds. P. Bjorntrop and S. Rössner. London: J Libbey, pp. 281–6.

[14] Caterson, I.D. and Broom, J. (eds) (2001). *Pocket Picture Guide to Obesity*. London: Harcourt Health Communications.

[15] The Counterweight Project Team (In press). Exploring the experiences and views of weight management from practice staff involved in the Counterweight programme. *Family Practice*.

[16] Ditschuneit, H.H. (2006). Do meal replacement drinks have a role in diabetes management? *Nestle Nutrition Workshop Series. Clinical & Performance Programme*, vol. 11, pp. 171–9; discussion pp.179–81.

[17] Truby, H., Baic, S., deLooy, A., Fox, K.R., Livingstone, M.B., Logan, C.M., Macdonald, I.A., Morgan, L.M., Taylor, M.A. and Millward, D.J. (2006). Randomised controlled trial of four commercial weight loss programmes in the UK: initial findings from the BBC 'diet trials'. *BMJ (Clinical research ed.)*, 332: 1309–14.

[18] NICE guidelines (2007). http://www.nice.org.uk/search/guidancesearchresults.jsp?keywords = obesity& searchType = guidance (last accessed 19 January 2009).

Chapter 6
Obesity and weight loss: Myths and reality
Alexandra M. Johnstone and Sue Bird

With the increased prevalence of obesity has come a frantic search for the ultimate treatment option. Obesity and excessive weight gain does not happen overnight and therefore the solution is not a 'quick fix'. There are many treatment options available, with a lack of scientific evidence as to which diets are best for an individual. In this chapter, the concept of energy balance is described relative to energy requirements and research findings are summarised, emphasising that weight loss can be achieved under the right conditions. However, there are a lot of misconceptions or myths associated with obesity and weight loss and these will be explored from a scientific perspective.

Obesity has now grown to be a major health issue worldwide and for the first time the number of people who are overweight is greater than the number who are starving. In England, the prevalence of overweight trebled between the years of 1980 and 1998, with 17 per cent of men and 21 per cent of women classified as overweight or obese. If these figures aren't bad enough, they are worse elsewhere, such as in the USA, where in some states, more than half of the population are classified as being overweight. In the UK, these figures have real consequences at a government and individual level, costing the NHS an estimated £0.5 billion per annum in direct healthcare costs for treating the consequences of obesity.

What weight should I be?

What weight should I be?

There is no 'ideal body weight'. Instead health professionals look at a range of healthy weights which reflect the lowest risk of ill health. Other factors, such as age, smoking status, fitness and family history, will determine the overall health of an individual. Body mass index (BMI) is a simple ratio of weight-for-height that is commonly used to classify overweight and obesity in adults at a population level. It is calculated as the weight in kilograms divided by the square of the height in metres (kg/m^2). For example, an adult who weighs 70 kg and whose height is 1.75 m, will have a BMI of 22.9, being classified as normal/healthy weight for height according to the WHO and NIH classification. The limitations of BMI are discussed in Chapter 3.

Having dispensed with the notion of a perfect weight for any individual, let us proceed to deal with the myths which beset the area, and examine each in turn, questioning whether or not each has any foundation.

Exploding myths

Obesity is a serious medical condition and there are lots of anecdotal reports about why some people find it difficult to lose weight and keep the weight off in the long term. There are many reasons why people would prefer to ignore their expanding waistline, preferring to think that their 'clothes have shrunk in the wash'. Sometimes there are genuine medical reasons for weight gain, but often it is simply an issue of overeating relative to energy expenditure. Some of the anecdotal reasons will be examined in more detail using scientific data to examine the credibility of the myth. With all good myths, there is sometimes a shred of truth in the argument.

Myth 1:
'I only have to look at a cream cake to gain weight'

This could also be described as 'my friend eats the same as me but never puts on weight'. This implies that some people gain weight more easily than others, and led to the concept of 'small and large eaters' in the 1980s. It was thought that the small eaters had lower energy expenditure, making them predisposed to gaining weight. However, it is widely recognised that getting people to report their habitual food intake accurately is almost impossible. This problem is referred to as mis-reporting or under-reporting food intake. This could be due either to the technical difficulties of actually weighing everything you eat and drink or to cognitive restraint because we don't want to admit to eating five chocolate biscuits in one go!

Figure 6.1   **Anecdotal reasons why we can't lose weight**

Figure 6.2   **Measuring actual food intake (accurately recording/remembering your intake is difficult?**

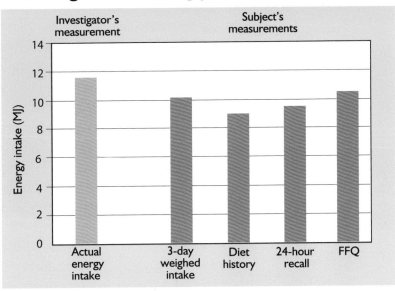

Figure 6.2 shows some data collected from the Rowett Research Institute on a group of male and female subjects living at the Human Nutrition Unit for a few days (data courtesy of Dr Leona O'Reilly, Rowett Research Institute). The subjects were asked to record or recall their food intake, but they were unaware that the investigator had already weighed all their food before they got up in the morning. The investigator-weighed food intake, shown in the brown column, is greater than all the other methods where the information came from the volunteer, including a 3-day weighed intake, a diet history interview, food frequency questionnaire (FFQ) and a 24-hour recall. On average, all the methods relying on the subject led to some degree of under-reporting of food intake. This is common in all dietary surveys and it is difficult to eradicate.

So, this author (AMJ) would always encourage people who believe that they 'don't eat much' but put on weight easily, to find out what their portion sizes are and how much they eat and drink, not forgetting that alcohol contains energy. Also, they should remember that it may be that the friend who is slim and eats the same as they do at lunchtime also takes regular exercise and, although he or she may eat a similar amount, they will burn off more energy through physical activity.

Myth 1 is FALSE – everyone will gain weight if their energy intake is more than their energy expenditure.

Myth 2: *'I have a slow metabolic rate'*

First, it is necessary to define what metabolic rate is. Basal metabolic rate, or BMR, is the minimum energy requirement required to sustain life at rest. Put simply, it is the amount of energy expended by the body to remain in bed, at rest, all day, maintaining digestive processes and organs. It can be easily measured in the laboratory using a 'ventilated hood', which is a form of indirect calorimetry (see Figure 6.3). You can think of the human body as an engine, where the fuel (food) is burned to generate energy and, as mammals, we produce carbon dioxide and water and consume oxygen. The amount of these gases produced is directly related to the amount of fuel being utilised by the body. These laws of thermodynamics are well established in physics. A BMR measurement is usually conducted first thing in the morning, after an overnight fast, and in a thermoneutral room so that there is no shivering or sweating. The measurement is conducted after a short rest, and it takes between 30 and 40 minutes. The subject lies under a ventilated hood, and samples of gaseous exchange are measured, under standardised conditions. The investigator will obtain a printout of amount (ml) of the respiratory gases (oxygen consumed and carbon dioxide produced), which is used to calculate basal energy expenditure, or BMR.

Figure 6.3   **Measuring metabolic rate in the laboratory**

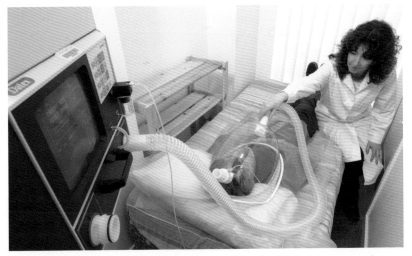

A: A subject undergoing a metabolic rate measurement, with the amount of oxygen consumed and carbon dioxide produced being monitored.

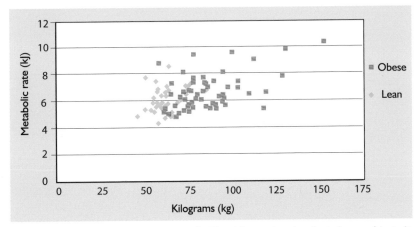

B: Resting metabolic rate in a group of 150 subjects, showing that obese subjects in pink have a higher metabolic rate than the lean subjects in blue.

BMR is highly dependent on body size and body composition. Obese subjects have a higher BMR in comparison to lean subjects.

This is clearly seen in Figure 6.3, where the obese subjects (pink dots) have a higher metabolic rate than lean subjects (blue dots), simply because they have a larger body. Analogously, if a lean subject was given a sack of potatoes to carry around for a day, then he/she would expend more energy. BMR is not only dependent on body size; the composition of the body is also important. The more lean (muscle) tissue, the greater the BMR, because muscle is metabolically active, relative to fat mass. There are some well-known medical exceptions, where a person's metabolism is altered due to hormonal or endocrine disturbance, such as in thyroid disease. However, these can be easily detected by a doctor conducting a blood test.

Metabolic rate can be estimated by general equations, such as the Schofield equations [1] (Table 6.1).

Table 6.1

Equations for estimating the basal metabolic rate (BMR) in megajoules per day (MJ/d), where W is weight in kg

Males

10–17 years	$BMR = 0.074W + 2.754$
18–29 years	$BMR = 0.063W + 2.896$
30–59 years	$BMR = 0.048W + 3.653$
60–74 years	$BMR = 0.0499W + 3.930$
75+ years	$BMR = 0.0350W + 3.434$

Females

10–17 years	$BMR = 0.056W + 2.898$
18–29 years	$BMR = 0.062W + 2.036$
30–59 years	$BMR = 0.034W + 3.538$
60–74 years	$BMR = 0.0386W + 2.875$
75+ years	$BMR = 0.0410W + 2.610$

You can estimate your daily energy requirements by multiplying your BMR by a factor that relates to your level of physical activity. Today, we often have a sedentary lifestyle, and live in what some people have called an 'obesogenic environment' [2].

Most people use the ratio of 1.4–1.6 x BMR, which equates to 140 to 160 per cent of their BMR for daily activities in work and leisure. The best way to find out your daily energy requirements is to weigh yourself at the beginning and end of a week, before eating and after emptying the bladder, and simultaneously record an accurate food diary to record all energy intake. If you remain weight stable then you are likely to be in energy balance; if you lose weight then you are eating less than your energy requirements.

Myth 2 is FALSE – metabolic rate can be measured or estimated with relative accuracy and is dependent on body size and composition and, when corrected for body composition, metabolic rate does not vary between individuals.

Myth 3: *'I'm not fat, I have big bones'*

When you weigh yourself on the scales and the result is more than you thought or would like, what do you do? Some people blame the scales, or take all their clothes off to try and convince themselves that they weigh less. Instead of accepting that they are carrying excessive body fat, others imply that it is because they have 'heavy bones'. It is true that some people can have a 'slight frame' and others may have a 'heavy build', and this will also impact on how much muscle mass you carry. There are methods of measuring frame size using calipers or a tape measure but, by directly measuring bone mineral mass, we can get an indication of the variability of this component of body composition.

We can use low-dose radiation to measure bone mineral mass, and an image of the scanner and the resultant images are shownin Figure 6.4. Dual energy x-ray absorptiometry (DXA) is most commonly used to assess bone mineral content in the spine in the context of osteoporosis risk. However, many machines can also measure whole-body bone mineral content (BMC) and because x-rays are absorbed differently by bone and soft tissues, DXA can also be used to estimate regional body composition (e.g. limbs, head, trunk, abdomen) and fat mass.

Results from the DXA scanner for bone mineral content show that minerals account for a small proportion of the human body. For example:

- An adult female weighing around 60 kg will have about 2.5 kg of bone mineral content = 4 per cent total weight
- An adult male weighing around 75 kg will have about 3.5 kg of bone mineral content = 4 per cent total weight

It follows that people who are taller will have more bone mass. This

Figure 6.4   **Dual energy x-ray absorptiometry (DXA)**

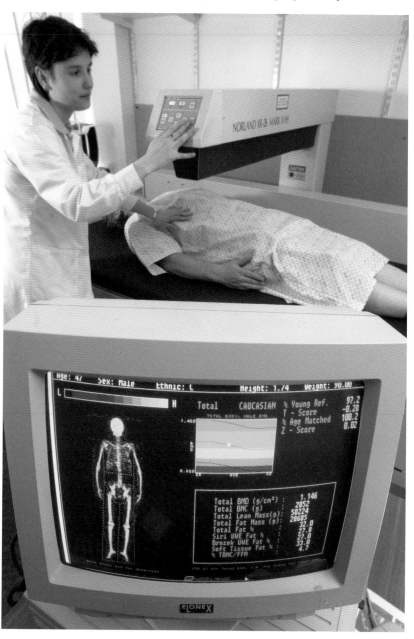

does not equate to the weight of a skeleton (because this is mineral weight – not the weight of the bones) but serves as an example of the variability of bone mass. Bones include collagen (a protein) and water, contain marrow (fat) and are linked with connective tissue (ligaments), which can be included in skeletal mass. When we consider body composition, water is in fact the largest component, being 60–70 per cent of the weight of the body mass (Chapter 3 details the chemical model of body composition).

Myth 3 is FALSE – excess weight is unlikely to be explained by extreme bone mass.

Myth 4: *'This is my natural weight'*

It is interesting that some animals are naturally able to regulate their body weight according to the season or photoperiod (the amount of daylight and dark). For example, the Siberian hamster (Phodopus sungorus) uses photoperiod to adjust the level of its body mass. In the summer they have a dark coat and are heavier; in the winter they have a pale coat and are leaner (see Figure 6.5, data courtesy of Dr Julian Mercer, Rowett Research Institute). Even though they have ample food, they can make anticipatory changes in food intake and body weight relative to daylight hours, having somehow a means to regulate energy intake and body weight. This is shown in the plot in Figure 6.5, where the short day animal (SD, winter) loses weight despite having ample food and the long day (LD, summer) animal is able to regulate its food intake to maintain body weight.

Figure 6.5

The Siberian hamster is a seasonal model of body weight regulation

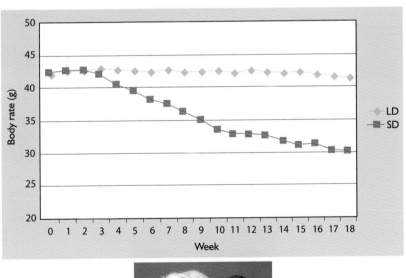

Winter (lean)   Summer (obese)
Light coat   *Dark coat*

In humans, there was a theory in the 1970s and 1980s that we had a pre-determined 'set point' for body weight, which was the weight at which our body would 'naturally' be maintained. The inference from this was that dieting would be ineffective because people would bounce back to their 'set point'. However, there is no concrete evidence of one set-point control model in humans, rather an acceptance that control of body weight is multi-factorial. Seasonal animals remain of interest to nutrition scientists, however, because they provide a useful model to examine novel components of the body weight regulatory system, which may have applications in humans.

Myth 4 is FALSE – humans are unlikely to have a set point of body weight.

Myth 5: *'Rapid weight loss is all water loss anyway'*

Obese people often want a quick cure and to lose weight rapidly and they will resort to extremely restrictive regimes to achieve this. Although a reduction in body weight as a numerical value on the scales is encouraging, weight loss should optimise fat loss to improve health. We conducted a series of studies to look at how body composition changed with a rapid, moderate and slow rate of weight loss. We considered this in a series of three weight loss studies in three groups of obese men, in the following format:

- Study 1 – Rapid rate: achieving a nominal 5 per cent (6.1 kg) weight loss in 6 days
- Study 2 – Moderate rate: achieving a nominal 10 per cent (9.2 kg) weight loss in 3 weeks
- Study 3 – Slow rate: achieving a nominal 10 per cent (12.6 kg) weight loss in 6 weeks

Figure 6.6 shows the weight loss at 5 per cent in men, and how much of this was due to water loss. It is clear that in the rapid weight loss regime, over 50 per cent of the weight loss was due to water loss. In this regime, the water loss is associated with the depletion of glycogen stores in the liver. These data indicate that the slowest rate of weight loss promoted a minimal loss in water mass and incidentally, maximal loss of fat mass. A fast rate of weight loss was only a quick fix, with minimal impact on reducing fat mass.

Figure 6.6   **Body composition change with slow, moderate and fast weight loss.**

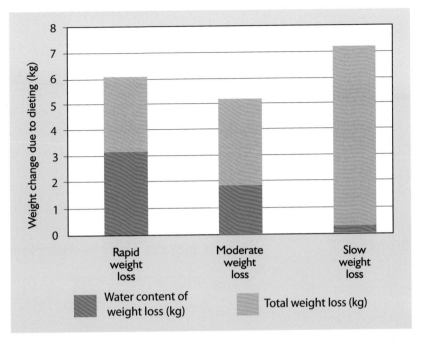

Myth 5 is TRUE – rapid weight loss often invokes a greater loss of water mass, likely to be linked to mobilisation of muscle mass and/or glycogen stores. One should therefore opt for a slower rate of weight loss to enhance fat mass loss.

Myth 6: *'Once I lose weight, I regain it'*

Yo-yo dieting, whereby weight is lost and then often re-gained in excess, with body mass going up and down over the years, may have a negative impact on health or well-being [3]. In terms of solving the obesity epidemic, different therapies are required at different stages: (i) prevention, (ii) treatment and (iii) maintenance of body weight after weight loss. The clinical approach to obesity therapy pre-dates the scientific era, with Hippocrates suggesting in the fifth century BC that:

Obese people and those desiring to lose weight should perform hard work before food. Meals should be taken after exertion and while still panting from fatigue and with no other refreshment before meals except only wine, diluted and slightly cold. Their meals should be prepared with sesame or seasoning and other similar substances and be of a fatty nature as people get thus satiated with little food. They should, moreover, eat only once a day and take no baths and walk naked as long as possible [4].

The concepts of increasing energy expenditure, limiting food intake and appetite control are to be found even in this era. Unfortunately, in the present day, we still do not have the magic bullet or pill that obese people crave to solve their obesity problem. Obesity is a problem that occurs over years, with people often gaining weight steadily. For example, a women with a BMI of 21 who gains a relatively small amount of weight, say 2.5 kg a year (5.5 lb), from now on, would be overweight in three years, and obese in seven years. A key message is to weigh yourself regularly and to halt the upward incline of weight by eating a healthy diet and maintaining levels of physical activity.

Figure 6.7   **Weight regain after weight loss**

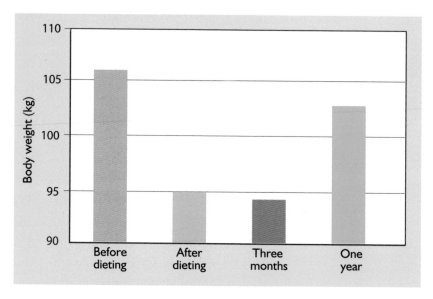

Unfortunately it is true that most of the subjects who lose weight by participating in Rowett diet trials, will regain it, in the long term. Figure 6.7 shows that in a group of men who participated in a Rowett study, most of them remained leaner for up to three months, then regained weight over a year. In terms of obesity therapy that is effective in the long term, surgery such as gastric by-pass and banding has been shown to be effective over a ten-year period [5]. However, surgery is the last resort for clinicians to suggest as a therapy and may not be suitable for all patients because of the psychological and metabolic side-effects.

Myth 6 is TRUE – most people who lose weight regain it. More research is required to understand the physiological and psychological risk factors for this.

Myth 7: *'Losing weight is difficult because I feel tired'*

If there are negative psychological consequences of weight loss, then this will limit the success of the regime. The human body is designed to defend body weight, stemming from the 'hunter-gatherer' era where food provision was sparse, with times of feast and famine [6]. Biologically, it is more difficult to lose weight than it is to gain weight. The human body's appetite system is designed to protect us from weight loss, sending signals to either increase food intake or reduce energy expenditure [7]. One of the anecdotally reported consequences of weight loss is feeling fatigue or tiredness, whether this is in the form of mental alertness or reduced physical ability. Ironically, fatigue can be the result of either an excessive energy intake (think of Christmas day) or a depleted energy intake.

We considered this in the same series of three weight loss studies in three groups of men, in the following format:

- Study 1 – Six consecutive days of total starvation, achieving a 5 per cent (6.1 kg) weight loss.
- Study 2 – Three weeks on a very-low-energy-diet (VLCD, 2.5 MJ/d) achieving a 10 per cent (9.2 kg) weight loss.
- Study 3 – Six weeks on a low-energy-diet (LCD, 5.0 MJ/d) achieving a 10 per cent (12.6 kg) weight loss.

Within our own study, subjective fatigue was measured hourly during waking hours, using visual analogue scale (VAS) questionnaires, where the subjects were asked to rate their degree of tiredness from, 'As fatigued as I have ever felt' to 'Not at all fatigued'. The data are shown in Figure 6.8 for the starvation group who were given water only. The data in Figure 6.8 indicate that for fasted subjects there was a significant increase in fatigue in response to the starvation and that feelings of fatigue remained elevated for some time when normal eating was resumed. Within the VLCD group, fatigue increased during the first half of weight loss (but to a lesser extent than for the fasting group), but these feelings were abolished during the last 10 days of weight loss, returning to baseline levels. The LCD group report fatigue being unchanged throughout the study. This finding may be important to highlight to dieters, since it may be that a period of adaptation is required for subjects to become accustomed to an increased exercise and reduced intake regime.

Figure 6.8

Subjectively rated fatigue before, during and after weight loss

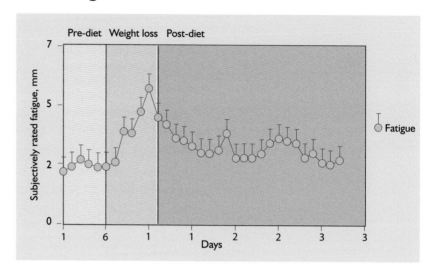

In order to avoid fatigue, lose weight at a slow rate of loss, at around 1–2 kg a week.

Myth 7 is TRUE – rapid weight loss can make you feel tired and irritable. Aim at a small but steady weight loss to avoid fatigue, rather than crash dieting.

Myth 8: *'It's all in my genes, Doctor'*

Heritability studies in humans have shown that there is a genetic component in body weight, fat mass, FFM (fat-free mass) and fat distribution [8]. However, this biological inheritance accounts for only 20 to 30 per cent of these variables. The variation in the deposition of body fat may be attributable to a complex relationship between genetic, nutritional, metabolic, psychological and social variables. There are more than 250 genes identified as markers for obesity [9]. Single (major) gene defects may cause obesity directly (for example, leptin deficiency in humans [10]); however, these cases are comparatively rare and can certainly not account for the increased prevalence of obesity in the global population.

The evidence suggests that environmental factors are of more importance than genetic determinants in the development of obesity. This view is also supported by the fact that obesity has been rapidly increasing within a comparatively short time period and in the face of a rather constant gene pool. It is currently considered that a genetic predisposition may render some individuals more susceptible to weight gain than others when exposed to an environment such as, for instance, a high-fat diet [11,12]. Much work is now focused on gene-nutrient interactions and defining the obese phenotype. When we know more about obesity phenotypes, we will be in a position to target individualised prevention or weight loss therapy.

Myth 8 is FALSE – major gene defects are unlikely to be the cause of obesity in the general population. However, it is true that you can have a genetic predisposition to gain weight in the right environment.

Myth 9: *'Weight loss lowers my metabolism'*

Figure 6.9

Measuring metabolic rate before and after weight loss

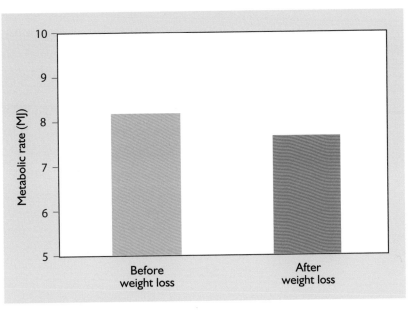

We discussed in Myth 2 that larger people have a higher metabolic rate than smaller people, and so it follows that when you lose weight, your metabolic rate will decline. The amount it declines will be dependent on the amount of weight loss (kg), the composition of the weight loss (fat or lean tissue), the macronutrient composition of the weight loss diet (protein, fat and carbohydrate content) and the level of physical activity or exercise. Figure 6.9 show a simple graph of metabolic rate (BMR) from a group of male subjects before and after a 10 per cent weight loss ($\sim$10 kg). As they lost weight, their energy requirements also dropped. As an aside, this may be one of the contributing reasons why some people plateau with weight loss: as they become smaller, their energy deficit also becomes smaller if their dietary intake stays the same. Also, if subjects go back to eating what they did before weight loss, then they will gain weight, as they require less energy to maintain a stable body weight.

Myth 9 is TRUE – weight loss does lower metabolic rate.

Conclusion

Losing weight in theory is simple, as long as energy intake is lower than energy expenditure. However, in practice, this is difficult to achieve and maintain over a prolonged period of time. One of the themes of my obesity research at the Rowett Research Institute is a focus on what controls hunger, appetite or motivation to eat as a means to understand how to improve compliance to achieve weight loss. The problem is that there are many external (environmental) and internal (biological and psychological) influences on what and why we eat, which makes us all complicated systems. Eating should be enjoyable and it is possible to achieve this and still lose weight to improve health.

References

[1] Department of Health (1991). *Dietary reference values for food energy and nutrients for the United Kingdom*. Report 41 of the Panel on Dietary Reference Values of the Committee on Medical Aspects of Food Policy. London: HMSO.

[2] Brownell, K.D. (2002). Genetic influences on body weight. In Fairburn, C.G. and Brownell, K.D. (eds), *Eating disorders and obesity: a comprehensive handbook*. New York: Guilford Press, pp. 16–21.

[3] British Nutrition Foundation (1999). *Obesity*, London: Blackwell Science, pp. 132–7.

[4] Bray, G.A., Bouchard, C. and James, W.P.T. (1997). *Handbook of Obesity*. New York: Marcel Dekker, pp. 1–29.

[5] Ryden, A. and Torgerson, J.S. (2006). The Swedish Obese Subjects Study – what has been accomplished to date? *Surgery for Obesity and Related Diseases* 2(5): 549–60.

[6] O'Keefe, J.H. Jr and Cordain, L. (2004). Cardiovascular disease resulting from a diet and lifestyle at odds with our Paleolithic genome: how to become a 21st-century hunter-gatherer. *Mayo Clinic Proceedings* 79(1): 101–8.

[7] Blundell, J.E. and Gillett, A. (2001). Control of food intake in the obese. *Obesity Research* 9 Suppl 4: 263S–270S

[8] Bouchard, C. and Pérusse, L. (1988). Heritability and body fat. *Annual Nutrition Reviews* 8: 258–77.

[9] Rankinen, T., Zuberi, A., Chagnon, Y.C., Weisnagel, S.J., Argyropoulos, G., Walts, B., Pérusse, L. and Bouchard, C. (2006). The human obesity gene map: the 2005 update. *Obesity* 14(4): 529–644.

[10] O'Rahilly, S. (1998). Life without leptin. *Nature* 392 (6674): 330–1.

[11] Bray, G.A. (1990). Obesity. In M.L. Brown (ed.), *Present Knowledge in Nutrition*. Washington, DC: International Life Sciences Institute Nutrition Foundation, pp. 23–38.

[12] World Health Organization (1999). *Obesity: Preventing and Managing the Global Epidemic*. Report of a WHO Consultation on Obesity, Geneva 3–5 June 1999. Geneva (WHO/NUT/NCD/98.1).

Chapter 7
The 'patient's' perspective: A lifelong struggle with weight

Diane Finegood

As far back as I can remember I have been overweight and like most overweight people I thought it was my fault. If I just had more will power, if I just tried harder, I too could be a normal weight person. I now understand that obesity is a complex problem with many determinants and requires solutions relevant to complex problems. I also understand that our genes and our environment are important in addition to personal will, knowledge and desire. I am not sure I could identify all of the specific factors that led me to become obese, but it doesn't really matter. What matters is that I now understand that, by changing my environment and by finding easy-to-adopt ways to increase my level of activity and decrease my calorie intake, I can sustain a healthier body weight for the rest of my life.

My first attempts at weight loss were before I even entered my teen years. Along with my mother, I entered the Weight Watchers programme countless times. I associated weight loss with a specific diet regimen or programme, with going to meetings, and with being able to have friends and self-esteem. I gave little thought to maintaining the weight I would lose. From my teens until my twenties I attended Weight Watchers at various times and I tried many of the fad diets of the day to drop the excess pounds. At the age of seventeen, after losing 40 lb (18 kg) yet again, I even sought to reinforce my self-esteem by entering a Weight Watchers Teen Queen contest. But like most people who embark on diets, I was trapped in a cycle of weight loss and weight gain – usually gaining more than I had lost. When I was in my mid-twenties and a graduate student in physiology, I made a last-ditch effort to find love. I joined Weight Watchers one last time, lost another 40 lb and got down to a size sixteen.

As a graduate student I was studying the physiology of insulin resistance and diabetes. I was well aware that obesity put me at an increased risk of developing diabetes and many other chronic diseases. Although I understood these risks and the connections between obesity and diabetes, the knowledge I had did not stimulate weight loss nor did it provide me with an understanding of how to lose weight and keep it off. I still believed if I just worked harder at dieting I too could be thin. I still believed that weight loss was achieved by going on a diet because that's what dieting was for. Although I understood that my family history of obesity played a role, I still thought that having the will to eat less was more significant and I only had myself to blame if I was overweight. It was not yet common to recognise that many aspects of our day-to-day surroundings contribute to weight gain and that maintaining a healthy weight requires multiple sustainable changes in behaviour. Sick of the weight loss and weight gain cycle, I decided to stop dieting. Gradually over the next fifteen years I gained on average five lb (2.2 kg) a year, eventually reaching a size twenty-four. Although this weight gain was not as rapid as I had previously experienced, the year-after-year compounding of weight was clearly not a healthy trend. Notwithstanding the weight gain, I did find love and with it some of that elusive self-esteem.

By the time I reached my early forties, I was in a longstanding committed relationship, a successful scientist working on the physiology of diabetes and weighed in at about 250 lb (113 kg). Our understanding of the causes and consequences of obesity was beginning to change, but the prevailing sense was that although diets were useful for weight reduction, most dieters regained their weight. At that time the notion that only moderate reductions in weight were required to achieve health benefits, such as a reduced risk of developing diabetes, were starting to emerge. Our understanding and attitudes towards weight loss began to change, thanks to the results of the Diabetes Prevention Program Trial (DPPT) and its demonstration that lifestyle intervention (150 minutes per week of moderate intensity physical activity such as brisk walking and a weight loss goal of 7 per cent of body weight) reduced the incidence of Type 2 diabetes by 58 per cent in individuals at high risk of developing the disease [1]. So by separating the health benefits of moderate physical activity and a healthy diet from the need to look slim and trim, I began to think that maybe it was time to develop a healthier lifestyle.

Armed with the results of the DPPT and other similar trials, a family history of Type 2 diabetes and the sense that I could change my lifestyle, rather than go on a diet, I was ready to stop my weight gain and start on a path towards a healthier body weight. Given my long history as a dieter, I still thought I should start with dietary modifications and given the predominant belief that low-fat diets are healthier, I started to remove fats from my diet. Since my focus was on changing behaviour, I was careful to stay away from the scale to gauge my weight loss. I knew from my personal history that for me the scale triggered emotions and reactions that were counterproductive to losing weight and feeling good about the process. As I began to lose weight, instead of constantly using the scale, I paid more attention to how my clothes fitted and how I progressively felt better in them and ultimately how the clothes started to outgrow me.

By reducing my intake of fats I was able to begin losing weight, but after a weight loss of about 20lb (9 kg) I reached a plateau. Although I no longer craved fatty foods, my intake of carbohydrates had probably increased. Also my background in engineering and physiology helped me to understand that while I had reduced my overall energy intake, with weight loss, I was also reducing my overall energy expenditure because I didn't require as many calories to move my lighter body around. In essence I had reached a new steady state. In order to trigger further weight loss I realised I needed to adopt another behaviour change to either increase calories burned or decrease the number of calories I took in. It became clear to me that with a sustainable healthy lifestyle as my goal I needed to keep adding new behaviours to the ones that were becoming second nature in order to keep the weight loss momentum going. I turned to physical activity in order to set the weight loss wheels in motion once again. I began walking on a treadmill. Initially, I used the calorie-counter to monitor how much energy I burned. This turned out to be a mistake because burning significant numbers of calories is a difficult task. They add up very quickly through food and drink consumption, but it takes hours to work them off. By fixating myself on burning calories, I pushed myself too long and too hard on the treadmill. This made physical activity a daunting task, one I had to constantly motivate myself to do, and as a result I became less and less consistent as the days progressed.

At that time I was introduced to pedometers (step counters) and the idea that one can set incremental step goals. By counting steps instead of calories I got focused on the behaviour, not its consequences, and started to set more realistic incremental goals. This allowed me to make my exercise sessions more enjoyable because I could slow the treadmill down, still work up a sweat, and I could read while getting in my exercise. This really helped me to pass the time and shifted my attention from thinking about how much longer I could stand doing that bout of exercise and instead look forward to spending some time with a good book. There were other unexpected benefits of using the pedometer. This simple tool helped me to realise that by changing other day-to-day routines I could increase my physical activity levels. For instance I started parking further away from my office to increase my daily step count. I also began taking stairs instead of using elevators. While I realised that not all steps are created equal, by focusing on steps I was able to consistently increase my activity level. These incremental changes over time helped me lose more weight.

When I reached my next plateau or new steady state, I knew it was time once again to find a new behaviour change to adopt. I decided to refocus on my food intake. Since I was on a low-fat nutrition programme, I tended to derive a substantial portion of my energy intake from carbohydrates. I thus made the conscious decision to increase my fruit and vegetable consumption and my protein intake to reduce my reliance on carbohydrates. I also began implementing the 'volumetric approach', which suggests that by decreasing the calorie density of food you can trigger satiety at a lower calorie intake. After reading a paper by Barbara Rolls, which demonstrated that people who ate soup (with 8 oz/226 g of water) instead of a casserole with the equivalent number of calories ate less afterwards [2], I started to make soup for lunch every day. Instead of taking a large container of leftovers for lunch, I started taking one that was half the size and at work I added a bouillon cube and water to turn it into soup. This definitely reduced my lunchtime calorie consumption and to my surprise I was less hungry later in the day as dinnertime approached.

With time I lost more weight and added new healthy behaviours. At one point the weight loss stagnated for a longer period and I had to think about ways to increase my energy expenditure when I already committed significant time to walking on the treadmill and I was working at a very busy job that required significant amounts of travel. I turned to jogging so I could burn more calories in less time. Running instead of walking presented an unexpected challenge and an unintended consequence. The challenge was I could no longer read to pass the time and if I didn't occupy my mind I would focus on how much I disliked what I was doing! Fortunately rapid advances in digital technology provided the answer in the form of public radio podcasts. Armed with an MP3 player and the latest downloads, I could catch up on what was happening in the world while increasing my energy expenditure. Initially I was disappointed to learn that becoming a runner didn't have the expected result of more weight loss, but I did begin to convert fat into muscle and my waistline started to change.

Unfortunately, when I started running I became less consistent in getting at least 10,000 steps everyday. Unconsciously I was giving myself a break. While I would always get 10,000 steps on days that I ran, on other days I generally did not achieve this goal and as a result, running didn't lead to an increase in total energy expenditure. By returning to a focus on my pedometer, I renewed my commitment to getting 10,000 steps most days of the week. As a result I now find myself each morning thinking 'where am I going to get my steps today?' On some days it is going for a run, on others I walk to and from work (forty-five minutes up and down the side of a mountain) or if neither of these are possible I take a walk with the dog or go on the treadmill after dinner. When I travel I try to stay at hotels that have a gym with a treadmill or are at a bit of a distance from where I have to go.

My travels down the road of progressive behaviour change coincided with a new job, one that ultimately intersected closely with this weight loss journey. After starting my lifestyle modification, I was named Scientific Director of a new national institute supporting research on nutrition, metabolism and diabetes. The Institute identified obesity and healthy body weight as its sole strategic priority which helped me to stay on course in my efforts to adopt a healthy lifestyle. I also had a great opportunity to learn more about the problem of obesity from a broad range of perspectives. Through this academic journey I came to learn what I intuitively understood as an individual who struggled with weight issues, namely that obesity is a complex problem with many different determinants and no single or simple solution.

At the roots of weight gain and obesity are hundreds of individual and societal factors that affect our food and physical activity behaviours. For each individual a certain combination of these many factors affects our ability to make healthy choices. For me the issues included having a thrifty genotype (i.e. I don't need as many calories as the average adult woman to maintain my body weight), having a sedentary lifestyle, having ingrained habits that included lots of snacking, especially at night while watching TV, and having a diet that didn't include many fruits or vegetables. Like many I also have a sweet tooth. For others the problem may be working two sedentary jobs to make ends meet, not earning enough money to access healthy foods, juggling family responsibilities that make exercising on a daily basis impossible, or driving an hour to work each way surrounded by messages which encourage excessive eating.

We can't take the individual out of the healthy lifestyle equation, but we must acknowledge how our environments affect our choices and behaviours. Once we open our eyes to the intersection between individuals and their environments in the context of obesity or weight gain, we can better draw a path towards making the healthy choice the easy choice. It is a matter of matching an individual's capacity to act to the complexity of their task. In my case, although I didn't understand it at the time, taking a step-by-step approach to behaviour change helped me reduce the complexity of my task by tackling one behaviour at a time until it was part of my natural routine. By making sustainable behaviour changes I was integrating them into my regular or normal routine and essentially making them 'mindless tasks'.

Adopting a healthy lifestyle has been a back and forth learning journey and I continue to push myself to find new behaviour changes or modify existing ones to keep my weight loss or maintenance momentum going. Through this journey I have retained several key lessons that I try to keep in mind as I continue to strive to maintain a healthy lifestyle. Successful adoption of a healthy lifestyle requires conscious commitment and a focus on the behaviour changes themselves and not the outcomes alone. Counting calories burned or weight lost on a scale is less effective or motivating than how my clothes feel. I also found that behaviour change must be something I can incorporate into my lifestyle and maintain for the rest of my life. This means finding ways to make the boring or monotonous more fun or engaging. It also means finding practical tools or solutions to help me gauge my food intake and physical activity levels. I started using a pedometer to keep track of the number of steps I took and I used a food log to monitor my calorie intake. The reason for using such tools is to monitor the behaviour not the outcome. Sustaining behaviour changes is also a function of how artificial they are. This is why fad diets and physical activities that cannot be incorporated into your schedule and lifestyle don't work. It is important to start with small changes that progressively become a normal part of your routine and then, as you reach a steady state, incorporate another change. Following this progressive pattern and rhythm helps build motivation and improves one's capacity to adopt and maintain a healthy lifestyle.

Conclusion

At this point in my journey I have lost more than 70 lb (32 kg) over an eight-year period and reached a size sixteen. I maintain a consistent level of physical activity through running and walking but I continue to struggle to lower my food intake. Although I know that the body mass index is really only useful as an index of obesity across populations, mine sits at the high end of the overweight range and I was hoping to get it down to the normal weight range. While I try to use a variety of approaches to 'mindful eating' such as using smaller plates and ensuring half my plate is covered with vegetables and no more than a quarter is protein and a quarter carbohydrates, I know that if I want to reduce my food intake enough to lose more weight, I will need to count calories and limit myself to about 1,500 calories per day. Although this is less than what is recommended for someone of my age, gender and height, it is what my genetics seem to demand. Regardless of whether or not I am able to lose more weight, I am today a much healthier and more confident individual. I know that my lifestyle has reduced my risk of developing some of the chronic diseases that run in my family and I am confident this is a lifestyle I will maintain for the rest of my life.

References

[1] Diabetes Prevention Program Group (2002). Reduction in the incidence of type 2 diabetes with lifestyle intervention or metformin. *New England Journal of Medicine* **346**: 393–403.

[2] Rolls, B., Bell, E.A., and Thorwart, M.L. (1999). Water incorporated into a food but not served with a food decreases energy intake in lean women. *American Journal of Clinical Nutrition* **70**: 448–55.

Acknowledgments

I would like to thank my Research Assistant, Jasmine Sharma, for her invaluable writing and editorial support on this chapter.

Chapter 8
The 'patient' and the 'expert' working together in weight management
Maria McQuigg

Previous chapters have highlighted the increasing problem of the obesity epidemic both for society and for the individual. While the argument carries on as to whether obesity is a social or medical problem, the NHS is treating the consequences of the obesity epidemic such as high blood pressure, diabetes, heart disease, and joint pain, to name just a few. We have a situation in which obesity needs to be treated; however, there are limited resources to do anything other than treat the consequences. In this chapter we shall discuss the treatment of obesity from the perspective of the relationship between the patient and the dietician, and the many barriers and limitations we are both up against in the management of this chronic disease.

Obesity is a clinical term used when a person's weight is high enough to pose a significant health risk. Health professionals use the term obesity in the clinical sense, but to our patients it can be seen as a derogatory term, alluding to their physical appearance. This clinical label has a loaded meaning for patients, especially if expressed in a seemingly judgemental manner.

Obesity could be termed a lifestyle disease, with a perception that the fault lies with the patients themselves. It is true, we are all responsible for our own food choices; however, given that the rate of obesity has trebled over the last twenty years, can we really say that over this time, as a nation, we are all of a sudden simply letting go, giving in to a greedy and slothful existence? Over half the UK population are either overweight or obese, and on average gaining a kilogram in weight every year [1,2]. This is the direct result of the imbalance between the energy or calories we are taking in and the energy or calories we are burning off in the form of activity. A weight gain of 1 kg in a year equates to just 20extra calories a day that we are not burning off as energy. In reality this equates to less than half a plain biscuit extra a day that we are not burning off.

Statistics are very interesting for health professionals, but ultimately what does this mean for the overweight or obese individual? First, you are not alone, and secondly, just a few small changes to the calories taken in, and the calories expended on a regular basis can make a huge difference. We simply need to eat a little less and do a little more. The slimming industry is a multi-million pound industry with a new diet appearing almost every month, all promising guaranteed weight loss. No matter how these diets are presented, what food they contain and in what order, fundamentally they are promoting fewer calories eaten and more calories expended. This sounds simple. However, anyone who has ever tried to lose weight will confirm it's not that easy. Losing weight is often accompanied with major highs when diet and activity changes are easy and exciting, often followed by major lows or lapses when the occasional slip becomes a complete U-turn back into old habits. Quick-fix weight losses are often followed by weight gains, in which the individual quickly returns to their original weight or often, heavier, with deflating effects on morale.

Dieticians are perceived as the experts in obesity management, skilled in relating the latest research findings to practical dietary changes for patients in their care. Finding evidence-based programmes for weight management is not as easy as it may sound. With regard to food, everyone eats and most take some interest in what they are eating, and express an opinion as to food choices. Indeed it seems we are all our own experts when it comes to nutrition. This is particularly confusing when it comes to messages given relating to food. We are bombarded with messages from our schools, families, communities, healthcare services and the media. Given so many messages telling us what is good for us, you can imagine there are more than a few inconsistencies. These can mean that patients often become confused and more defensive of their own established lifestyle choices.

Dieticians are trained to give advice based on the scientific evidence and what is perceived to be in the patient's best interest. This scenario centres on a one-way relationship in which the patient is seen as powerless. Consider the situation in which a patient visits the dietician for a twenty-minute session every two months. This equates to just 0.02 per cent of the patient's life in two months; the other 99.99 per cent of their time they are living their own lives, dealing with personal pressures and influences intheir work and home environments that are perhaps the real reason for their weight problem. We are in the caring profession, and it is our job to help people. Rather than highlighting the problem and coming up with solutions for the patient to fix their medical condition, we should be encouraging patients to take control and responsibility for themselves, enabling them to make their own choices, for the 99.98 per cent of their time that they are not in the presence of a dietician.

Beginning

Beginning

The working relationship between the dietician and the patient should have a beginning, a middle and an ending. When a patient first comes to see a dietician there is very real potential for a clash of expectations, based on first impressions and personal experiences, with many patients coming in expecting to be told how to lose weight. It is worth taking time to discuss these expectations. In the NHS, due to sheer numbers, time pressures, and an eagerness to help, this introductory phase is often overlooked, and we dive straight into giving helpful advice. Patients' expectations are rarely sought, nor are patients given an opportunity to express their anxieties. Whether we realise it or not, patients are expected to adopt a powerless role in the healthcare system, which can be an anxious setting for many. They first confront receptionists, the gatekeepers of the reception area, before seeing the health professionals who will treat them. Contrary to popular opinion, many receptionists are trained to actively listen to patients' queries and be empathetic to their needs. Potentially the patient could be put at ease by reception staff and directed to the waiting area to wait, only to find that they are unable to find a chair they can sit on. All too often in obesity clinics there are still few chairs large enough, which has the effect of humiliating the patient. It is worth taking the time and effort to consider these aspects when a patient initially comes for support.

This is the opportunity to redress the power imbalance, and exhibit warmth and equality, before the patient attends their appointment with the dietician. Patients have often battled with their weight for many years and it is important to give them the time and space to speak, and tell their own story. It has now been recognised that dieticians may benefit from adopting a counselling skills approach to enable them to actively listen to their patients. Indeed this is becoming a vital part of dietetic practice. The dietician is encouraged to show continuing empathy, putting their own experiences and reality to the side and trying to sense and respond to the experiences and perceptions of the patient. Empathy is not a single response but a process of being with the client. The patient must feel understood for empathy to have an impact and the basic attending and responding skills of active listening, verbal and non-verbal reflection and summarising to tease out feelings and communicate these back to the patient are essential for this process. It is difficult sometimes to find the right words to express the way we feel, and the non-verbal cues are often better predictors of true feelings than the words spoken. This includes the use of silences, which few of us are comfortable with; however, it is often these very silences that can be the starting point for many patients to gather their emotions and words together to discuss issues that are important to them. It is a useful exercise even in everyday scenarios to allow silences. Silences allow the speaker to gather often very emotive thoughts.

Considering how personal and sensitive our relationship with food is, it is essential to allow this expression of thoughts and feelings with our patients. Good non-verbal attending includes good eye contact, facial expressions that often mirror the patient's emotions without the need for words and a posture that is open, relaxed and not slouched. How often have you been spoken to, and the person speaking has not looked up nor given you any eye contact while they are continuing with another job that they have to do? It is not a welcoming approach, nor one in which you are going to feel that you are being listened to. Indeed this is an approach used commonly in the health service due to the necessity of recording tasks and data on computer screens while the patient is in front of us, and the pressures of time in the clinical settings. However, this begs the question: Are we there for the patient's needs or is the patient there for ours?

Using the verbal and non-verbal skills of attending to a patient, we are able to reflect back to the patient that their words and feelings have been heard. It is like holding a mirror before the patient so that they can see themselves more clearly [3]. This is a sure sign that we as dieticians are actively listening to our patients and conveying empathy. The focus is on the emotional content of what is being said, teasing out both the positive and negative. This is important when listening to a patient for negative thought patterns that may relate to negative lifestyle habits such as binge eating, or inactivity. It is important to be able to reflect back these feelings to enable the patient themselves to see how these feelings may be affecting them emotionally and physically. Armed with just a few of the tools adopted when taking on a counselling approach, the dietician is able to let the patient speak about the history of their own weight problem, and try to gain an understanding of how their weight and relationship with food is affecting their life. Why do they want to lose weight? Is it appearance, social pressure, health, or some other reason? What have been their weight loss attempts in the past, and have they achieved the targets that they set themselves or those that were set for them?

It is useful to identify often unrealistic weight loss goals at this stage, and discuss the patient's own expectations of weight loss. Often these unrealistic weight loss goals may relate to some other aspect of their lives, and are not connected to their weight directly. If a person starts from the basis of feeling they are a lesser person because of their weight, and live in fear of being judged by their weight or appearance, ironically, it is this very lack of self-esteem that is likely to lead them to eat more. The patient may benefit by identifying key motivations other than how they look, such as, health, physical fitness or just feeling better mentally within themselves. It is best to encourage the patient to make positive changes in their own right, rather than expect these changes to come about naturally as a result of weight loss, as they may be disillusioned. It is also good to discuss at this stage how the patient feels regarding their weight and whether it may be holding them back from achieving other seemingly non-weight-related goals.

The primary aim of these initial sessions is that patients believe that they are able to control their weight and also accept weight stability rather than weight loss if need be. It is necessary to ascertain how strongly a patient feels about losing weight. Why are they preparing themselves to put this degree of effort into a lifestyle change? What do they expect to get out of it, and how important is that to them? It is also worth considering a patient's confidence. Given that many patients now referred to see a dietician may have had many attempts at trying to lose weight throughout their lives, it is necessary to ascertain how confident they feel that they are able to achieve and maintain modest weight losses. If confidence is very low in this regard, it may be worth spending time discussing what it would take for them to increase it. What support, both medically and socially, would be needed to achieve this? This time spent initially with the patient is invaluable. A patient's lack of confidence may in part be due to a lowered self-esteem, where repeated attempts to lose weight in the past have failed, and indeed resulted in them being heavier than they have ever been. The ball is put back in the patient's court, regarding the lifestyle changes they feel they would be able to tackle at this stage in their lives. A useful strategy is to discuss any residual ambivalence at this stage. What are the advantages (what the patient may gain from making such a change) compared to the disadvantages (what they would lose if they were to make this change)? An example is presented in Table 8.1.

Table 8.1

Advantages and disadvantages: Stop nibbling on crisps in the evening.

Advantages What might I gain from changing?	Disadvantages What might I lose from changing?
● Lose weight	● I enjoy crisps while watching TV
● Feel more in control	● I would miss them
● Feel healthier	● Wouldn't know what to do with my hands in the evening
● Might help my skin	● The physical effort required to make the changes

If there are more advantages than disadvantages, then the individual is ready to tackle the change. If a person is in the frame of mind in which they are ready, the time is right, they feel it is an important change that they want to make, and they feel confident that they are able to make small changes to their lifestyle, they will view the disadvantages as barriers that can be overcome rather than excuses that they use to prevent action.

The challenge for the dietician is to be able to develop their interpersonal and communication skills, to be able to actively listen to their patients. The dietician's ability to conduct this counselling approach in practice is very dependent on knowing their own limits in terms of competency and physical and emotional availability. This can be supported by formal supervision in the workplace and in some dietetic departments they are now offering 'buddy' type support in this area to improve counselling skills in practice. Many dieticians are also encouraged to keep reflective diaries of current practice to enable them to learn from their own experiences and develop their own self-awareness when they are treating obese patients. There is a real risk that without these supervisory and support mechanisms in place the dietician may become overwhelmed, stressed and demoralised and this can ultimately affect patient care.

The key elements in empowering patients to regain control over their own health behaviours are frequent contact and support. Many patients prefer to have structure and it is therefore useful to further clarify expectations as to the possible number of sessions, if using a structured programme of weight management, and the duration of each session. A necessary boundary at this stage is timing, with assurances to the patients that sessions will begin and end at the allotted times and encouragement of punctuality. Patients continually running late, armed with excuses each time, or not turning up at all raises alarm bells about their commitment to the programme. It is often good to have written information, encouraging discussion of the methods of practice, duration of appointments and limitations of sessions, and ensuring the understanding of the patient. The issue of confidentiality is an important ethical point that must be respected in any session using a counselling approach. It is vital that the patient feels safe, and in an environment where they are able to explore personal issues. Given that food, weight and body shape are very personal and sensitive issues, it is important to provide an environment in which the patient can explore issues that are closest to them.

Middle

Middle

There is an ongoing development of trust between the dietician and the patient, leading to mutuality [4]. The patient feels safe in the confidential environment created, and trusts the dietician, which allows for a deeper exploration of the sensitive issues surrounding the patient's weight problem. In some cases this can lead into a cognitive behavioural approach in which it is not enough for patients to 'talk' about their problems; They also need to learn their way out of them [5]. The aim of the behavioural component is to enable clients to exercise more control over their behaviours. There is an educational bias to this approach, with the setting and implementing of mutually negotiated goals. The cognitive element is concerned with the thinking aspects of patients' experiences, much of which may have been touched on in the introductory sessions, but may be further explored as the sessions continue. This cognitive behavioural approach is more directive, and the dietician ideally must be trained in the theory and competent in its delivery. The patient is expected to complete assigned tasks, and there is an element of advice-giving. With the established mutuality already developed, there is an assurance that advice is being provided that is solely in the patient's best interest and not the dietician's.

Structured weight management sessions should include lesson plans, and ideally cover healthy eating, calorie deficit type plans, physical activity advice, dealing with negative thought patterns, and relapse prevention. The principal components of the behavioural contents are keeping food and activity diaries, the setting of Specific, Measurable, Achievable, Realistic and Time-bound (SMART) goals, lessons on nutrition with an emphasis on appropriate food choices, portion sizes, controlling urges to eat, and cognitive restructuring. Involving supportive family and friends at this stage is also beneficial, and in some cases also helps to promote healthier lifestyle choices in them.

Sessions continue to deal with motivational issues. Motivation is a fluid trait; it changes with the tide so one initial assessment may not mean that the patient will stay motivated for the duration of the sessions. Patients are encouraged to keep food and activity diaries which provide a basis to help them control their intake, but also to learn from previous experiences. Diaries can help the patient to learn their weaknesses, such as eating in the evening or when stressed or feeling low. The diaries can be used as a positive influence, to emphasise the positive changes that have been made as opposed to the occasional slip, thus helping to maintain a positive and realistic perspective on the lifestyle changes they are making. Food and activity diaries can also help us to understand the internal and external eating triggers. Feelings of hunger and satiety are the prime physiological reasons for eating behaviour, and the behavioural component enables patients to once again get in touch with these natural feelings of hunger and fullness. It also helps to distinguish between the internal triggers, including hunger, but also (often negative) emotions, and external triggers in our environment that promote eating.

It could be said that no-one can physically cause us to feel emotions such as anger, frustration or stress; we do this to ourselves, so how can we encourage patients to better manage these emotions without the drive to eat? How can we manage our environments better to make the healthier and more active choices the easier choices? Nutrition education is given to help provide the patient with the skills required to make healthier, lower-fat, lower-energy food choices. Advice is given on strategies to manipulate different foods, meal choices and portion sizes to create an energy deficit suitable for their daily living requirements, and encourage modest weight losses of 1–2 lb (0.4–0.9 kg) per week. These skills also provide the patient with the knowledge and the confidence to understand food labels and choose wisely from the vast array of convenient food choices available from many shopping outlets.

The patient is the person in control when setting their own SMART goals and this is helped by keeping a food and activity diary. Goals are continually reviewed by both the patient and the dietician over time, with a graded approach to changing habits. Unrealistically high or severe goals may lead to disappointment. It is important to empower the patient in these decisions regarding what they feel is acceptable for them. An important aspect of the cognitive behavioural approach is to look at the stimuli in our environments that prompt us to eat. The television is one of the most common triggers or stimuli to eat in society today. We are not born with these inherent urges to eat once the TV is switched on; these are learned responses over time, often over decades. The good news is that these learned behaviours can be unlearned.

Stimulus control involves the patient becoming aware of the associations, such as TV watching and snacking, and learning strategies to deal with them. In this example it could be watching less TV, doing another distracting activity while watching, such as puzzles, jigsaws, sewing or knitting. There are many other stimuli that affect different patients but no matter what they are, keeping a food and activity diary helps to highlight these and enable the patient to come up with their own strategies to learn new healthier behaviours.

With any weight loss programme, lapses are par for the course. Patients are encouraged to acknowledge them and discuss how to plan for these lapses in the future. It is good to discuss lapses at the start of treatment as many patients seen by the dietician have lapsed in previous weight loss attempts, and part of their lack of confidence is due to a fear of lapsing again. This has the real potential to be a 'self-fulfilling prophecy'. With this thinking, the chances are they *will* lapse, further enhancing their belief that they have no willpower and no control, and further undermining their self-esteem and confidence. It is possible to use the person-centred counselling approach to actively listen to the patient to uncover their feelings towards the prospect of a lapse, and the food diaries to enable the patients themselves to uncover the triggers for these lapses. The dietician's role is to empower the patient to exercise some personal control over what may have felt like a powerless situation in the past.

Ending

Endings

Much effort has been made by both the dietician and the patient to establish trust and mutuality to enable the patient to understand the roots of their weight problem, and empower them to make the necessary lifestyle changes to help them manage their condition. The ending of this relationship is just as important as the beginning, in which patients have been equipped with the skills to enable them to maintain their lifestyle changes and ultimately their weight. However, many patients drop out of weight management sessions before reaching this final stage. Perhaps they felt their problems were not being fixed as quickly as anticipated, had unrealistic expectations of weight loss, or perhaps were just not ready to make the efforts required to change their lifestyle. Whatever the reason, there are lessons for the health service in this area, and rather than diving straight into giving dietary and activity advice to patients, it may be worth spending some time with patients when they are first referred to ascertain their weight history, experiences, and their own personal expectations and motivations for trying to lose weight. Some patients, however, may prefer a more directive approach and being told what to do, and may be disappointed at the counselling skills approach taken, which is another reason to ascertain what patient expectations and preferences may be.

Conclusion

Obesity is a chronic, relapsing disease that is at epidemic levels, with many of its causative roots firmly placed in society. Obesity management in the NHS is taking on a more three-dimensional behavioural approach. Patients are being empowered with the skills to enable them to change their food and activity choices in their current environment. They are supported in making small changes in their lifestyle to achieve medically beneficial weight losses of 5–10 per cent and to maintain these losses. The management of the obese patient is taken through different stages in which the quality of the relationship between the dietician and patient is crucial, allowing the establishment of trust and mutuality. The area of obesity management is truly evolving, with more and more dieticians being trained in the use of counselling skills and adopting a behavioural approach to support patients in making lifestyle changes. Along with these changes in approach, there is an increasing emphasis in the health service on dieticians developing their self-awareness and understanding their potential effects on patients. This involves supervision in the workplace and the use of reflective learning logs so that as dieticians we can learn from our patients, just as our patients can learn from us.

References

[1] Heitman, B.L. and Garby, L. (1999). Patterns of long-term weight changes in overweight developing Danish men and women aged between 30 and 60 years. *International Journal of Obesity and Related Metabolic Disorders* 23: 1074–8.

[2] Norman, J.E., Bild, D., Lewis, C.E., Liu, K. and Smith West, D. (2003). The impact of weight change on cardiovascular disease risk factors in young black and white adults: the CARDIA study. *International Journal of Obesity* 27: 369–76.

[3] Rogers, C. (1991). *Client Centred Therapy*. London: Constable.

[4] Mearns, D. and Thorne, B. (1999). *Person Centred Counselling in Action*. 2nd edition. London: Sage Publications.

[5] Hough, M. (1998). *Counselling Skills and Theory*. London: Hodder & Stoughton.

Chapter 9
Physical inactivity, appetite regulation and obesity

Neil King, Rachel Colley, Nuala Byrne,
Andrew Hills, John Blundell

The evidence supporting the role of physical activity in the promotion of positive health and prevention of morbidity is well accepted [1]. Despite the robustness and unequivocal nature of this association between physical activity and health, it has only been in existence for half a century. It was seminal work by Morris [2] that generated interest in the link between inactivity and ill health. The evidence originated from the finding that inactive bus drivers had higher rates of coronary heart disease than their active counterparts – the bus conductors. The rationale was that the higher activity inherent in the role of the bus conductor contributed to their improved health. These data involved occupation-enforced inactivity, whereas we are now living in an environment (occupation and leisure) which imposes an inactive lifestyle.

A combination of environmental pressures, technological factors and societal transitions are likely to promote sedentary behaviour that could potentially lead to weight gain. Adults and children are susceptible to a technologically changing environment that facilitates an inactive lifestyle. Cultural changes are responsible for 'engineering' spontaneous physical activity out of the daily lives of many [1]. The indication is that collectively, to function in today's environment, behaviours predominantly involve minimal energy expenditure. Therefore, it is difficult to dispute that the environment exerts a strong influence on physical activity, and that today's environment promotes inactivity rather than activity. Cultural and lifestyle changes have led to a decrease in spontaneous and incidental physical activity [1]. Therefore, an inactive lifestyle is facilitated by the environment which could lead to a decrease in daily energy expenditure, thus increasing the probability of a positive energy balance and susceptibility to gain weight. From an epidemiological perspective, there is some ambiguity about attributing the increasing prevalence of obesity to an increase in inactivity. However, there is very clear evidence [1] that a reduction in physical activity (i.e. decrease in energy expenditure) does not down-regulate food intake.

Inactivity: biological and environmental forces

There are strong environmental forces that nurture inactivity. Indeed, there is a bias towards under-activity rather than activity. Table 9.1 summarises the occurrence and intensity of signals associated with eating and physical activity behaviours. From a behavioural perspective, it can be argued that there are very weak cues to promote activity and very strong signals to curtail activity – at least in the short term. Unlike eating, there is no strong biological drive to be active if periods of activity do not occur. The analogy with eating is that if food intake is abstained from, there is a strong drive (i.e. hunger) to eat – hence a strong biological reminder to eat. Physical activity is a volitional behaviour. Leading an active lifestyle requires motivation and effort. Inactivity is not a behaviour that is difficult to tolerate – indeed, it is a relatively easy habit to maintain. It has been proposed that physical activity is biologically programmed and under homeostatic control, similar to blood glucose and body temperature [3]. The signals that bring physical activity, especially vigorous activity, to an end are relatively powerful. For example, muscle pain, hyperventilation, lactic acid accumulation, thermal stress are all examples of somatic responses which will eventually cause an acute period of activity to end. Therefore, it is not unreasonable to postulate that inactivity is facilitated by the absence of any real drivers to be active. Even if we are biologically programmed to be active, the current environment is gradually diluting any 'drive' or necessity to be active.

Table 9.1

The relative strengths and weaknesses of volitional behaviours, eating and exercise

	Exercise	Eating
Essential for maintenance of life	No	Yes
Drive signals	Weak	Strong
Cessation signals	Strong	Weak

Inactivity and evolution

Inactivity and evolution

Inactivity and evolution

The relative contribution of energy intake (EI) and energy expenditure (EE) to the current obesity epidemic is frequently debated. There are suggestions that a marked increase in food intake is to blame, while others point the finger at a decrease in energy expenditure as a result of a decline in physical activity. Of course, it is intuitive that changes in both EE and EI will influence energy balance, hence the propensity to gain weight – it is the relative contribution of each behaviour which is equivocal. By extrapolating from Paleolithic dietary and activity behaviours, anthropologists have estimated the marked alteration in the ratio of EE:EI in today's society [4]. Purely as a result of a reduction in hunter-gatherer type activity, habitual EE has decreased from 1000 kcal/d to 700 kcal/d. These comparisons also demonstrate that, due to the low-energy density of available foods, Stone Age people sourced plants with a high EI (energy capture) relative to energy expenditure. In Eaton's [5] seminal paper he concluded that 'human ancestors existed within a metabolic environment of high-energy throughput characterized by both greater energy intake and greater energy expenditure than now is the case'.

Figure 9.1

Example of energy intake and expenditure in 'hunter-gatherers' and in today's western societies
(data derived from Cordain [4].)

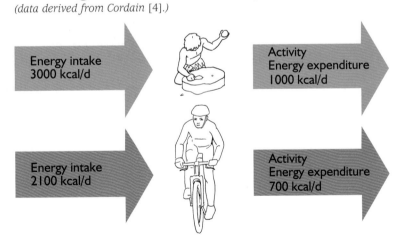

There is no doubt that minimal energy expenditure is required to sustain life in today's environment. The equivalent 'hunting and gathering' of food is considerably less energy demanding because of the readily available high-energy dense, snack foods. Combined with the labour-saving food preparation devices which are used in most homes in western societies, the energy cost of sourcing and preparing food is comparatively very low. Factor in the associated reduction in incidental and occupational energy expenditure and it is easy to accept that physical activity in today's society is lower compared with our ancestors.

There is currently a strong interest in assessing physical activity behaviours, particularly in children, in an attempt to determine the relationship between physical activity, EE and body weight. Despite the speculation and anecdotal evidence about physical activity levels in today's society, there is a lack of comparable and robust data to demonstrate that the actual level of physical activity (hence EE) is low compared with several decades ago. Of course, this is an area which has attracted some controversy, mainly because of the lack of a 'benchmark' of physical activity to compare current levels with. Most of the evidence for a reduction in EE comes from indirect surrogate measures. For example, there is evidence to suggest that the activity-energy expenditure of children getting to and from school has decreased as a result of more frequent car transportation [6].

Small screen recreation (SSR) is used to describe sedentary activities such as TV watching, playing video games and internet use. Many studies have attempted to determine the association between TV watching and obesity in children. Unfortunately, most of these provide cross-sectional data; hence they do not inform about the causal effects of TV watching on weight gain, so the evidence is equivocal [7]. More recently, longitudinal data demonstrated that lower SSR in adolescence was associated with lower prevalence of obesity, especially in females in adulthood [8]. It is inevitable that more time spent doing sedentary activities such as SSR inherently requires very low energy expenditure, displaces activity-induced higher EE and possibly leads to higher EI. However, this does not automatically imply that all inactive behaviours lead to weight gain.

Is weight gain a direct consequence of inactivity?

Weight gain and inactivity

Early work by Mayer in the 1950s contributed significantly to the understanding of physical activity, and body weight regulation. In their study of jute mill workers in West Bengal, Mayer *et al.* [9] found that EI only increases with activity within a certain zone of activity ('normal activity'), and that below this range ('sedentary zone') a decrease in activity is not associated with a decrease in EI. Rather, it is associated with an increase in EI combined with an increase in body weight. In essence, the principle of energy balance and body weight regulation is simple and based on EI being equal to EE. Any perturbations in EI or EE will inevitably lead to a shift in energy balance and body weight. The extent of the shift will be primarily influenced by the magnitude and temporal nature of the perturbations. However, if EI exceeds EE a positive energy balance occurs, which if it persists leads to weight gain. Although the general principles are simple, identifying the underlying factors and mechanisms which contribute to an imbalance between EE and EI is complex. Of course, inferences can be made from habitual activity in lean and obese individuals that inactivity leads to weight gain. However, direct longitudinal evidence demonstrating that inactivity inevitably leads to weight gain is more difficult. The problem is exacerbated by the limited methodology available to measure physical activity accurately and reliably. It is possible that sedentary and active behaviours can co-exist, and that one type of behaviour does not automatically displace the other. For example, it is possible for children to combine physically active behaviours (e.g. participate in sport and exercise) with sedentary behaviours (e.g. computer games, watching television) within the same day. Despite a lack of concrete and robust evidence to prove a causal association between inactivity and weight gain, it is intuitive that sedentary behaviours in children should be limited because of their contribution to a reduction in EE. One of the key features of sedentary behaviours is that they typically co-exist with eating, which in turn could augment the obesity epidemic.

Physical activity and appetite regulation: does inactivity reduce food intake?

Appetite regulation

Although the direct effects of inactivity on body weight are more difficult to ascertain, most of the evidence demonstrates that there is a weak coupling between activity-induced EE and EI [10]. This so-called 'loose coupling' between exercise-induced EE and EI has negative implications for a decrease in EE, especially when this is occurring naturally as a result of increased habitual inactivity. A decrease in EE is an automatic consequence in individuals who decrease their activity. There are convincing data to show that EI is not down-regulated with the reduced EE. Although these data originate from experiments in which inactivity is artificially simulated in a laboratory, it is probably reflecting what occurs in the free-living environment. By artificially imposing inactivity [11], it has been demonstrated that an activity-induced reduction in EE is not compensated for by a reduction in EI. Figure 9.2 shows clearly that, despite a marked reduction in EE (red bars) while resident in the whole body calorimeter compared with the free-living active (Act) treatments, participants did not down-regulate their EI (brown bars). Indeed, EI remained constant across all activity (Act and Sed) treatments, and was only affected by the high-fat (HF) dietary manipulation. Therefore, physical inactivity does not cause an automatic reduction in food intake. The implications for weight gain and obesity are of particular concern, especially in light of the evidence that inactivity-induced reductions in EE are occurring naturally in the free-living environment due to people becoming less active. To make the situation worse, eating tends to be a sedentary activity. Thus inactivity can promote weight gain by automatically decreasing EE while simultaneously increasing EI.

Figure 9.2

EE and EI under varying activity conditions

(Adapted from Murgatroyd et al. [11]. See text for a detailed description.)

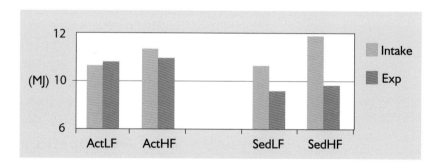

Does activity improve appetite and energy balance regulation?

Activity and appetite

It is feasible that habitual activity serves as a primer by constantly sensitising energy balance homeostasis by fine-tuning the appetite regulatory system. Therefore, habitually physically active individuals are better able to regulate their food intake and energy balance because of increased appetite sensitivity. Appetite sensitivity can be defined as the precision of the appetite regulatory system to detect alterations in food intake. Using cross-sectional data [12] demonstrated that habitually physically active individuals have a more accurate appetite regulatory system than habitually inactive individuals. Participants were provided with either a low- or high-energy preload for lunch, and were then allowed to eat from an *ad libitum* test meal buffet. The habitually inactive group were unable to differentiate between the two energy preloads, whereas the habitually active group detected a difference and compensated for the higher energy preload by decreasing their *ad libitum* intake (by approximately 90 per cent). This study suggests that activity increases the sensitivity to satiety signals, and that EI is more tightly regulated. The implication of these data is that physical inactivity could have a detrimental effect on energy balance and contribute to the increasing prevalence of obesity. A mis-match between the rate of eating-induced intake (calories consumed) relative to the energy cost of physical activity (calories expended) could potentially undermine the influence of exercise on energy balance and weight control. For a given amount of energy, the duration of exercise is markedly greater compared with the duration of eating. The rate of energy intake far exceeds the rate of energy expenditure. For example, to expend 600 kcal, an individual of moderate fitness (i.e. VO_2max 3L/min) would have to exercise for approximately 60 minutes at 75 per cent VO_2max. However, any individual (independent of aerobic fitness) could ingest 600 kcal of food energy in the form of an energy-dense snack in three to four minutes.

Compensatory responses – are perturbations in physical activity adjusted for?

Compensatory responses

Compensatory responses can be categorised into behavioural and metabolic and will influence the associations between activity, weight gain and obesity [13]. An increase in hunger and energy intake could compensate for any exercise-induced increase in EE, which, in part, could explain any lower than expected weight loss. The individual variability in compensatory responses is likely to explain why some people respond better than others to exercise. There is a need for more careful of monitoring of individuals who are more resistant to the beneficial effects, so that those who are more susceptible to compensating can be identified. It is commonly assumed that increased physical activity will lead to a net increase in EE. However, it is possible that imposed activity leads to inactivity. That is, physical activity interventions cause an increase in inactivity due to compensatory responses, such as reduced non-exercise activity thermogenesis (NEAT). Therefore, it is possible that in the free-living, naturally occurring environment, individual variability in NEAT contributes to energy balance and the susceptibility to gain weight.

Physical activity and body weight

Activity and body weight

A plethora of data exists which demonstrates an inverse relationship between habitual physical activity and anthropometric characteristics such as body mass index, body weight and body composition. Whether physical activity per se or inactivity (time spent sedentary) is the most important contributor to weight gain in children and adolescents has been examined in a series of independent studies. Of course, accurate and reliable measurements of total daily EE are rare and difficult to assess. Unfortunately, methodological limitations and variations in definitions of sedentary, moderate and vigorous activity compound the problem and add to the ambiguity.

The advent of accelerometers and improved technology has provided more detailed information about physical activity including the intensity and time spent inactive. Physical activity is not a dichotomous behavioural variable (i.e., active or inactive). The day-to-day and intra-individual variability in duration and intensity of physical activity behaviour suggests it is more variable. Although inactivity is relatively fixed and homogenous, physical activity involves a range of intensities, durations and periodicities. A recent study showed that there was a significant association between body mass index (BMI) and all ranges of activity, with the exception of sedentary time [14]. However, when the obese subjects' data only were included in the analysis there was a significant association between physical activity (PA) and BMI for all levels of activity, including sedentary.

A caveat with limiting the assessment of the association between BMI and PA is that it does not provide the whole picture because it commonly excludes measurement of EE. It is intuitive to expect that PA is a reciprocal of BMI, mainly because body weight could be a limiting factor in movement. However, a low PA does not automatically imply a low EE – i.e. physical activity is not equivalent to energy cost of activity. An elegant study conducted by Ekelund *et al.* [15] confirmed this phenomenon by comparing PA and EE between obese and lean adolescents. Using a novel combination of EE measured by doubly labelled water and PA measured by accelerometry, these data proved that, although PA was significantly lower in the obese, their corresponding EE did not differ.

Conclusion

A sedentary lifestyle is associated with chronic disease and ill health. The asymmetrical pressures imposed by the environment which facilitate inactivity whilst simultaneously providing an increased opportunity to over-consume food promote a susceptibility to gain weight. The inability of the appetite system to down-regulate food intake in response to inactivity compounds the problem. Exercise and dietary interventions could help by promoting a negative energy balance. However, individual variability and compensatory responses to energy balance perturbations need to be understood so that weight management can be tailored to suit individuals.

References

[1] Chakravarthy, M.V. and Booth, F.W. (2004). Eating, exercise, and 'thrifty' genotypes: connecting the dots toward an evolutionary understanding of modern chronic diseases. *Journal of Applied Physiology* 96: 3–10.

[2] Morris, J.N. and Crawford, M.D. (1958). Coronary heart disease and physical activity of work: evidence of a national necropsy survey. *British Medical Journal* 2: 1485–96.

[3] Rowland, T.W. (1998). The biological basis of physical activity. *Medicine and Science in Sports and Exercise* 30: 392–9.

[4] Cordain, L., Gotshall, R.W., Eaton, S.B. and Eaton, S.B. III (1998). Physical activity, energy expenditure and fitness: an evolutionary perspective. *International Journal of Sports Medicine* 19: 328–35.

[5] Eaton, B.S. (2006). The ancestral human diet: what was it and should it be a paradigm for contemporary nutrition? *Proceedings of the Nutrition Society* 65: 1–6.

[6] Harten, N. and Olds, T. (2004). Patterns of active transport in 11–12 year old Australian children. *Australian and New Zealand Journal of Public Health* 28:

167–72.

[7] Parsons, T.J., Power, C., Logan, S. and Summerbell, C. (1999). Childhood predictors of adult obesity: a systematic review. *International Journal of Obesity and Related Metabolic Disorders* 33: S1-S107.

[8] Boone, J.E., Gordon-Larson, P., Adair, L. and Popkin, B.M. (2007). Screen time and physical activity during adolescence: longitudinal effect on obesity in young children. *International Journal of Behavioral Nutrition and Physical Activity* 4: 26.

[9] Mayer, J., Roy, P. and Mitra, K.P. (1956). Relation between caloric intake, body weight, and physical work: studies in an industrial male population in West Bengal. *American Journal of Clinical Nutrition* 4: 169–74.

[10] Blundell, J.E., Stubbs, R.J., Hughes, D.A., Whybrow, S. and King, N.A. (2003). Cross talk between physical activity and appetite control: does physical activity stimulate appetite? *Proceedings of the Nutrition Society* 62: 651–61.

[11] Murgatroyd, P.R., Goldberg, G.R., Leahy, F.E., Gilsenan, M.B. and Prentice, A.M. (1999). Effects of inactivity and diet composition on human energy balance. *International Journal of Obesity and Related Metabolic Disorders* 23: 1269–75.

[12] Long, S.J., Hart, K. and Morgan, L.M. (2002). The ability of habitual exercisers to influence appetite and food intake in response to high- and low-energy preloads in man. *British Journal of Nutrition* 87: 517–23.

[13] King, N.A., Caudwell, P., Hopkins, M., Byrne, N.M., Colley, R., Hills, A.P., Stubbs, R.J. and Blundell, J.E. (2007). Automatic and volitional compensatory responses to exercise interventions: metabolic and behavioural barriers to weight loss. *Obesity* 15: 1373–83.

[14] Hemmingson, E. and Ekelund, U. (2007). Is the association between physical activity and body mass index obesity dependent? *International Journal of Obesity and Related Metabolic Disorders* 31: 663–8.

[15] Ekelund, E., Aman, J., Yngve, A., Renman, C., Westerterp, K. and Sjostrom, M. (2002). Physical activity but not energy expenditure is reduced in obese adolescents: a case-control study. *American Journal of Clinical Nutrition* 76: 935–41.

Chapter 10
Obesity, a psychological condition?

Lauren Puma, Christopher Ochner, Allan Geliebter

Obesity has become an epidemic in the USA, with 65 per cent of Americans being overweight or obese, and is rapidly spreading globally, recently leading to the new term 'globesity' [1]. According to the World Health Organization, 1.2 billion people in the world are overweight. The association between obesity and serious health conditions such as cardiovascular disease, stroke, hypertension, diabetes and cancer provides a major impetus for medical researchers to identify the factors that determine which individuals will eventually become obese.

In addition, research is currently underway to expand our knowledge of the psychological issues and psycho-pathology associated with obesity. Binge Eating Disorder (BED) and Night Eating Syndrome (NES) – two lesser known eating disorders – are more common among the obese than in the general population. With the number of overweight and obese individuals increasing, the number of these associated eating disorders is also increasing. These eating disorders may also contribute to the development of obesity or increase the severity of obesity. For the general public, much of what is known about obesity comes from watching television, surfing the internet, or personal experience. Aside from the documented health complications, obesity has been associated in the public mind with poor body image, low self-esteem, relationship and socialisation problems, and depression. This may be related to the common view that obesity is mainly a result of lethargy and a lack of willpower and is predominantly a psychological condition. The scientific review of the major psychological constructs and psychopathology associated with obesity presented in this chapter will challenge this conventional view.

History of the psychological constructs of obesity

Oral fixation

Oral fixation

In the beginning of the twentieth century, Sigmund Freud presented the psychosexual stage theory of human development. Within Freud's framework, obesity and other eating disorders resulted from disturbances during the oral phase. The oral phase, occurring in the first eighteen months of life, is the stage where pleasure is derived mainly from the mouth. Practitioners of Freudian psychoanalysis theorised that obese individuals were orally fixated as a result of emotional deprivations or excesses experienced during the oral stage. Freud's concept of libido paralleled that of hunger, a compelling sensation to seek out food. Many psychological impulses and conflicts could lead to overeating to diminish anxiety and guilt, and achieve pleasure. Obese people were considered to have a personality disturbance or emotional conflict. Currently, this Freudian perspective is considered outmoded but is seen as an early attempt at a psychological explanation for the development of obesity.

Psychosomatic theory

Psychosomatic theory

In the first half of the 1960s, the psychoanalyst Hilde Bruch observed that her obese patients literally did not know when they were physiologically hungry. Bruch theorised that the inability to identify hunger was rooted in childhood. When a mother disregarded her child's hunger signs (e.g. crying, irritability, etc.) and fed the child whenever she decided the time was right, the child's nutritional needs were inappropriately and inconsistently appeased. The child would then become an adult who responded only to external stimuli because of an inability to recognise appropriate internal sensations and feelings. Bruch proposed that obese individuals are unable to discriminate between hunger and states of fear, anger and anxiety, and may label almost any state of arousal as 'hunger'. Alternatively, they may label no internal state as 'hunger', resulting in reliance upon, and vulnerability to, external cues to eat. Unable to recognise when they are physiologically hungry, obese individuals may eat more frequently or consume larger portions than they physically need. This 'psychosomatic theory' posited that the inability to distinguish between hunger and negative emotional states leads to overeating when experiencing stress or bad moods.

Initial attempts to find support for psychosomatic theory, however, were unsuccessful.

Externality theory

Externality theory

By the end of the 1960s, psychologists had turned their attention to the 'externality theory', that Stanley Schachter had derived in part from Bruch, which highlighted a distinction between internal and external cues for eating behaviour. Internal cues are considered to be physiological feelings of hunger (e.g. stomach pangs, light-headedness, etc.) or feelings of fullness. External cues are present in the environment, and prompt eating, regardless of physiological hunger (e.g. TV images of good-tasting dishes, smells of foods, etc.). Schachter proposed that the eating behaviour of normal-weight people was primarily responsive to internal stimuli whereas that of overweight people was primarily controlled by external cues. This internal-external dichotomy stimulated further investigation into distinctions between the obese and normal-weight populations [2]. Subsequent research, however, showed that degree of overweight was not strongly related to the degree of external or internal responsiveness [3]. Thus, the proposed distinction between lean and obese individuals in responsiveness to internal vs. external cues did not appear to hold up.

An alternative explanation for differences between obese and normal-weight individuals' eating habits, derived from Richard Nisbett, suggested that the association between overweight and cue responsiveness was related to the 'set point', a genetically predetermined body weight. The inability for most people to maintain reductions in body weight was evidence of the set point. Attempts by obese people to diet and reduce the body below the set point would enhance external responsivity to food cues, and therefore weight loss would prove extremely difficult. Despite some scientific support, this perspective also lost ground because later studies [4] were unable to show that responsiveness to food cues consistently increased after weight loss.

Restraint theory

Restraint theory

When the externality theory of obesity began to fade, researchers began looking for another unifying theory. In contrast to psychosomatic and externality theories, restraint theory [5] proposed that overeating was a direct consequence of continual restriction of food intake. Inhibition of food intake made individuals susceptible to overconsumption in response to a stressor or 'disinhibitor' (i.e. alcohol, anxiety, or particularly the consumption of 'forbidden' foods). This 'disinhibited' eating was presumed to lead to the development of obesity and disordered eating. Restraint theory gained popularity in the 1970s and 1980s and helped spark an anti-dieting movement. Attempting to lose, or even control one's weight was seen as the cause of overeating, excess weight gain and obesity.

In recent decades, studies testing this theory, however, have revealed that overeating often precedes dieting. Michael Lowe and others have found that the tendency towards weight gain and binge eating cannot be accounted for by frequency of past or current dieting, as restraint theory would suggest [6]. Instead, researchers have noted a decrease in binge eating, along with an increase in dietary restraint, during dieting to lose weight. Eating behaviours described by restraint theory may instead reflect a pre-existing tendency towards overconsumption or 'predisposition' towards weight gain that could lead to excess body weight or obesity. Taken together, the available evidence suggests that dietary restraint itself may not be the causal factor leading to weight gain but typically represents an ineffective attempt to counter a predisposition towards overconsumption and weight gain.

Interestingly, the decline of restraint theory has led to a reconsideration of the externality theory. Those sensitive to external eating cues, especially in an environment saturated with eating triggers (e.g. fast-food restaurants, TV commercials depicting good-tasting foods, etc.) may practice dietary restraint in order to help control intake. However, this increased sensitivity to external cues or 'hyperresponsivity' is not proposed to explain obese vs. normal-weight differences. Judith Rodin, another Schachter student, maintained that external responsiveness leads to restrained and disinhibited eating in both normal and overweight people [7]. Lowe and colleagues have suggested that this hypersensitivity to external cues to eat contributes to, but does not necessarily cause, obesity.

Modern perspectives

Currently, most researchers have abandoned the idea of an all-encompassing theory to explain obesity as research reveals how complex and multi-faceted obesity is. Hyper-responsiveness to external eating cues may be one mechanism of action that can lead to either dietary restraint or to overeating. The long-term ineffectiveness of dieting suggests that attempts to regulate eating are not adequate in the presence of the 'obesigenic' [8] environment. Some obese, as well as normal weight individuals, who are at risk of becoming overweight, may tend to be more sensitive to external cues. Current research finds some support for elements of both the psychosomatic and the externality theory. Consistent with some aspects of the psychosomatic theory, emotional eating has been found to be a key driving force in overeating, especially binge eating. However, emotional eating is generally not viewed as misinterpreting emotions as hunger, but related more to conditioning. Palatable foods are rewarding and reinforcing, and emotional eating can serve to elevate low mood. Such emotional eating is successful in the short term and can perpetuate itself, but after a short while, mood often returns to the same low state. Schachter's theory of externality, while not applicable to the general obese population, may instead be pertinent to individuals with binge eating disorder who have multiple psychological problems. Since BED was not yet defined when Schachter's group conducted their studies, it is possible that a number of their obese participants had BED, and that some of their findings may be due to the BED subset. Currently, Schachter's theory is making something of a come-back, and indeed appears to be applicable to certain subsets, such as the BED population.

Given the increasing evidence for genetic heritability of obesity, it is likely that the biological theories, including the set point theory, account more strongly for the development of obesity than the psychological theories. Similarly, many researchers believe that no single intervention will prevent or successfully treat obesity. Now the focus is on how to properly integrate various perspectives, the psychological as well as the evolutionary, biological and environmental, as obesity is a derivative of these factors.

Additional factors related to obesity

Genetics

Genetics

Throughout most of human history, starvation, rather than obesity, has been the predominant threat to survival. This has led to the evolution of a 'thrifty' [9] phenotype that is energy-efficient and inclined to fat storage as proposed by James Neel. Humans appear to be predisposed to easily storing fat to increase the likelihood of survival during subsequent times of famine. Thousands of years ago, obese individuals would be more likely to survive through the harsh feast-famine cycles. However, in today's environment with plentiful and easily accessible high-calorie foods, the thrifty genes may be counterproductive and lead individuals to store a large amount of excess fat, which is difficult to lose. Current estimates of the genetic influence (heritability) of obesity range from 40 per cent to 60 per cent with the remainder accounted for by environmental, including some psychological, factors. Scientists are attempting to isolate both 'thin' and 'obese' genes. Most researchers support the idea that genetic factors determine a range of body weights or 'settling point' instead of a single set point. Although people do not have control over their settling point, the range may be large, with the environmental factors eventually determining actual body weight. Some researchers believe that bariatric surgeries (e.g. gastric bypass) in effect lower a person's settling point, facilitating weight loss (as much as 80 per cent of excess body weight) which can be maintained for years. Others believe that bariatric procedures allow individuals to reach the lowest end of their natural weight range.

An estimate of genetic predisposition towards weight gain can be ascertained by determining if one, or both, parents are/were lean or overweight. Twin studies have revealed a 40 per cent chance of becoming obese if one parent is obese and a doubling to 80 per cent if both parents are obese [10, 11]. Genes also play an important role in thinness, and those with two thin parents are much less likely to become overweight or obese. In addition, even behavioural factors, such as dietary preference for fats, degree of caloric compensation in response to food restriction, or inclination to engage in physical activity can reflect genetic predispositions. These genetically predetermined behaviours interact with environmental factors to eventually determine eating habits. Recognising that certain behaviours may have a genetic basis needs to be considered in targeting behaviour change [12].

Environment

Food environment

The food environment refers to the availability of different types of food and interacts with an individual's responsivity to external cues. In much of the USA, the food environment has been referred to as 'toxic' [13] or 'obesogenic' due to the abundance of readily available,

Environment

inexpensive, highly palatable, and highly energy-dense foods. Convenience and cost play important roles in dietary choices. In the current environment, it is more expensive, difficult, and time-consuming to prepare nutritious meals than it is to eat fast foods or frozen meals, which are often poor in nutritional value. This also translates to the individual household level if cabinets are filled with foods that are convenient to snack upon. Modifying personal food environments at home can be helpful because currently little has been done to modify the public food environment. However, efforts are underway to modify the environment as researchers are finding that environmental conditions are probably contributing to the obesity epidemic, including the relative high cost of such healthy foods as fruits and vegetables.

Modelling

Early in life, children learn to mould their behaviour by observing others, particularly parents, and mimicking and copying them. If parents pay little attention to nutrition or the macronutrient content of their diet, it is likely their child will also learn these indiscriminate eating behaviours. Attitudes toward food, choices in food selection, and timing of meals result in part from modelling such parental behaviours. As individuals reach adolescence, they also model their peers. Peer influence has been shown to have a large impact on eating behaviour. Overweight and obese girls have greater concerns about peer influence than do their normal-weight counterparts. Media images of thin movie actors and fashion models also can influence eating behaviour and heighten weight concerns. Peer groups and media images can lead young men and women to restrict their eating, which can result in unhealthy eating behaviours and excessive weight fluctuations.

Current research continues to investigate individual differences in susceptibility to internal (e.g. hunger) and external (e.g. palatable foods) stimuli. Modern neurophysiological studies [14–16] lend support to this distinction in identifying independent systems in the brain that contribute to eating behaviour. These studies indicate that the brain has an energy-regulating system, activated by food deprivation, and a pleasure system, triggered by the presence of palatable food. In the present food environment, eating may often be triggered by the pleasure system, rather than the hunger system. Leonard Epstein's group showed that food is more rewarding to obese than to normal weight individuals [17].

Associations have been made between food cravings and cravings for drugs of abuse, and evidence indicates some common pathways and activation of similar reward centres in the brain.

Culture

Different cultures vary in their attitudes to food, nutrition, eating and body weight. For example, in certain cultures, it is considered attractive for a woman to be full-figured whereas other cultures endorse a thin ideal. In many cultures, meals are synonymous with holidays and celebrations, and refusing food prepared by another may be considered rude. Many people have grown up eating food that is often fried or cooked in oil. By adapting food customs into healthier alternatives (e.g. baked vs. fried; poultry vs. beef) weight loss can be facilitated in a culturally sensitive manner.

Conclusions

The major factors that influence the development and maintenance of obesity are not independent of one another. Even with a genetic predisposition, it is not possible to become obese without an environment that facilitates it. It is the unique interplay of the psychological, genetic and environmental factors that ultimately determine who becomes overweight or obese.

Relationship between obesity and psychopathology

Obesity and psycho-pathology

Contrary to popular conception, Thomas Wadden and Albert Stunkard have noted that most obese people do not have diagnosable psychological disorders [18]. However, Binge Eating Disorder (BED) and Night Eating Syndrome (NES) are found in much greater proportion among obese individuals. Severely obese individuals (body mass index ≥ 40 kg/m^2) are even more likely to have these associated eating disorders and to suffer from more psychopathology.

Binge Eating Disorder

Binge eating

Binge eating was first described in 1959 by Stunkard and is characterised by eating, in a discrete period of time, an amount of food that is definitely larger than most people would eat under similar circumstances, accompanied by a sense of lack of control. Currently listed in the appendix of the Diagnostic and Statistical Manual of Mental Disorders (DSMIV-TR), Binge Eating Disorder (BED) is defined as recurrent episodes of binge eating (on at least two days per week for six months) in the absence of regular use of inappropriate compensatory behaviours, such as vomiting or using laxatives as seen in bulimia nervosa [19].

Prevalence

With more and more individuals becoming overweight or obese, the prevalence of BED is also increasing and receiving more attention. Approximately 33 per cent of obese individuals seeking weight loss treatment report some form of binge eating behaviour. The prevalence of BED ranges from 2 per cent in community samples to about 15 per cent in obesity clinics, and about 30 per cent among bariatric surgery patients. Unlike other eating disorders, BED is common in men, with a ratio of two to three compared to women. In addition, individuals who have BED typically remain symptomatic for about ten years, which is longer than seen in anorexia nervosa or bulimia nervosa.

Causes

As with most psychological disorders, genetic and environmental influences combine in the development of BED. Studies indicate a heritability of 40 per cent of BED. If only one parent has BED, the risk of developing BED doubles and the risk of obesity increases by 2.5 [20]. Children with one parent suffering from BED are more than twice as likely to develop BED and 2.5 times as likely to develop severe obesity (body mass index ≥ 40). Other factors such as environmental stress, parental and peer modelling, social influence, media messages, culture, and body image ultimately determine who develops BED.

A study conducted by Marci Gluck and Allan Geliebter at the New York Obesity Research Center tested the predisposition-stress theory by subjecting obese individuals with BED and without BED to a laboratory stressor (hands immersed in ice water for two minutes) in order to measure changes in appetite and cortisol. Both BED and non-BED subjects reported similar increases in stress after the cold sressor test, but the BED individuals had higher levels of cortisol in the blood, greater hunger, and greater desire to binge eat. This suggests that stress could be a major trigger for eating in BED [21]. Geliebter's group has also uncovered evidence of a larger stomach capacity in obese binge eaters. Stomach capacity in obese women was measured with a balloon inserted into the stomach after an overnight fast. On another day after a fast, the BED participants were instructed to drink a liquid test meal until they felt extremely full. Test meal intake was much larger in BED and correlated significantly with stomach capacity. There is also evidence in BED of an abnormality in the appetite hormone, ghrelin, produced by the stomach, as well as greater brain activation in response to binge type food stimuli, all of which support a biological basis [22].

The most common theory of how binge eating behaviours are maintained is based on the influence of negative emotions. Individuals who binge eat often attempt to restrict their eating for fear of gaining weight. They may be successful in restricting intake until they encounter some form of stressor such as eating a 'forbidden food'. Although binge eating often eventually leads to feelings of shame and guilt, it is the momentary elevation of mood that serves to reinforce and perpetuate the binge eating cycle.

Consequences

Although restraint theory posited that dietary restraint was the main cause of binge eating, more recent studies [23, 24] reveal that binge eating often precedes excess weight gain and initial dieting attempts. In community studies [25], more than 50 per cent of all BED cases are in lean individuals, who are at an increased risk for obesity. Obese individuals suffering from BED have a harder time losing weight, drop out more frequently from treatment, and show greater relapse than other obese individuals. Compared to normal obese subjects, obese BED participants consumed more calories during both binge meals and regular meals and experienced more frequent weight fluctuations. By definition, BED also causes marked psychological distress. Obese BED individuals have lower self-esteem and elevated levels of depression, anger, impulsivity, shape/weight-related distress, and overall psychopathology than do obese non-BED individuals. Significant relationships have been found between binge eating and the lifetime prevalence of major depression [26]. Although over-restrictive dieting may play some role in the development of BED, binge eating itself may contribute to attempts to further restrain eating. Similarly, negative emotions and body image disturbance can both contribute to the development of, and result from, binge eating.

Night Eating Syndrome

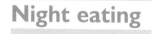
Night eating

While BED has been the subject of much new research in the past decade, Night Eating Syndrome (NES) is only now beginning to receive more attention although not listed at all in the DSMIV. NES has become more clearly defined as a pattern of delayed circadian intake of food, characterised by two main features: eating a substantial amount after dinner and awakening from sleep to eat, associated with trouble falling and staying asleep. According to O'Reardon and colleagues [27], NES is not only an eating disorder, but a mood and sleep disorder as well.

Prevalence

Similar to BED, NES is more prevalent in the obese than the normal-weight population, about 1.5 per cent in the general population and 10 per cent in obesity clinics. Studies show that among obese individuals seeking weight loss, NES prevalence is highest among the most severely obese.

Causes

Although less research has been done on NES than on BED, recent studies have shed some light on the causes of NES. Individuals with NES have lower levels of the hormone melatonin and higher levels of cortisol. Since melatonin helps to maintain the rhythmic cycle of sleeping and wakening, lower levels of melatonin may interfere with people's sleep patterns, resulting in insomnia and frequent waking throughout the night. Cortisol is produced by the adrenal glands, and when present in high levels in the blood may increase appetite. In addition, night eaters appear to have lower levels of the hormone leptin, which normally may suppress appetite at night during sleep, and thus may contribute to greater night-time awakenings to eat.

Night-time eating can also be viewed as a form of self-medication. People with an underlying mood disorder such as stress, anxiety or depression may be alleviating their symptoms with food, which can become self-perpetuating. Aside from eating irregularities, NES participants tend to be more depressed and have lower self-esteem than other obese people. Moreover, studies show that among obese individuals seeking weight loss, those with NES experienced less daytime hunger and ingested more food later in the day. They also lost less weight on a liquid formula diet, probably because they strayed from the diet at night. A restrictive diet during the day could inadvertently stimulate eating at night. Thus, in treating NES individuals, meal regulation without over-restriction is helpful. Recent findings also suggest that treatment with antidepressants, such as sertraline, may be effective. The emerging criteria for identifying individuals with

NES, supports its consideration as a listed eating disorder in the next edition of the DSM [28].

Differences between BED and NES

While both BED and NES may contribute to the development and maintenance of obesity, they differ in eating patterns and psychological characteristics. BED patients have more chaotic patterns (e.g. irregular meals, skipping meals) in addition to binge eating episodes. Binge eating occurs in relatively short episodes with large quantities of food eaten whereas NES usually involves continual snacking throughout evening hours. Although NES individuals may not experience binge episodes, many describe losing some control of eating after supper hours. In comparison to BED, NES individuals ate fewer meals during the first half of the day. They also continued to eat into the night with a significant number of nocturnal snacks which was much less likely in BED. The BED group described greater disinhibited eating and hunger and had more weight and shape concerns than the NES group and the comparison group [29].

Conclusion

This chapter has presented a brief overview of the psychological factors that contribute to, and result from, obesity. The psychological factors interact with the biological (genetic), and environmental variables that ultimately determine who becomes obese. With no single cause and no one overarching theory to explain obesity, it is unlikely that any one treatment will be effective. Obesity as such is not primarily a psychological condition, but is associated with more psychopathology when BED and NES are also present. BED and NES are currently under increased study, and will likely become better recognised in the DSMV which should provide further impetus for new treatments. Given that obesity is not simply a result of inadequate willpower, discrimination against obese individuals is inherently unfair. More multi-dimensional prevention and treatment programmes are needed to combat the obesity pandemic.

References

[1] World Health Organization (2008). Controlling the global obesity epidemic. http://www.worldwidewords.org/turnsofphrase/tp-glo2.htm Retrieved 9 May 2008.

[2] Schachter, S. (1968). Obesity and eating. *Science, New Series*, 161 (3843): 751–6.

[3] Rodin, J. (1981). Current status of the internal-external hypothesis for obesity: What went wrong? *The American Psychologist*, 36 (4), 361–372.

[4] Rodin, J., Slochower, J. and Fleming, B. (1977). Effects of degree of obesity, age of onset, and weight loss on responsiveness to sensory and external stimuli. *Journal of Comparative and Physiological Psychology*, 91 (3), 586–97.

[5] Polivy, J. and Herman, C.P. (1985). Dieting and binging. *American Psychologist* 40 (2): 193–201.

[6] Lowe, M. R. (1993). The effects of dieting on eating behavior: a three-factor model. *Psychological Bulletin* 114 (1): 100–21.

[7] Rodin, J. (1981). Current status of the internal-external hypothesis for obesity: What went wrong? *American Psychologist* 36 (4): 361–72.

[8] Brownell, K.D. (2002). Genetic influences on body weight. In Fairburn, C.G. and Brownell, K.D. (eds), *Eating Disorders and Obesity: A Comprehensive Handbook*. New York: Guilford Press, pp. 16-21.

[9] Neel, J.V. (1962). Diabetes mellitus: a 'thrifty' genotype rendered detrimental by 'progress'? *American Journal of Human Genetics* 14: 353–62.

[10] Mayer, J. (1965). Genetic factors in human obesity. *Annals of the New York Academy of Science*, 131, 412–421.

[11] Keller, C. and Stevens, K. (1996). Childhood obesity: Measurement and risk assessment. *Pediatric Nursing*, 22 (6), 494–8.

[12] Devlin, M.J, Yanovski, S.Z. and Wilson, G.T. (2000). Obesity: What mental health professionals need to know. *American Journal of Psychiatry* 157 (6): 854–66.

[13] Brownell, K.D. (2002). The environment and obesity. In Fairburn, C.G. and Brownell, K.D. (eds), *Eating Disorders and Obesity: A Comprehensive Handbook*. New York: Guilford Press, pp. 433–8.

[14] Beaver, J.D., Lawrence, A.D., van Ditzhuijzen, J., Davis M.H., Woods, A. and Calder, A.J. (2006). Individual differences in reward drive predict neural responses to images of food. *Journal of Neuroscience*, 26 (30), 7775–6.

[15] Scheurink, A. (2006). Eating, the second best thing in life. A neurobiological view on the pleasure of (over)eating. *Gedrag & Gezondheid: Tijdschrift voor Psychologie en Gezondheid*. 34 (2), 106–15.

[16] Lowe, Michael R., van Steenburgh, J., Ochner, C. and Coletta, M. (2009). Neural correlates of individual differences related to appetite. *Physiology & Behavior*, 97 (5), 561–71.

[17] Epstein, L.H., Leddy, J.J., Temple, J.L. and Faith, M.S. (2007). Food reinforcement and eating: A multilevel analysis. *Psychological Bulletin* 133 (5): 884–906.

[18] Wadden, T.A., & Stunkard, A.J. (2002). *Handbook of Obesity Treatment*. New York: Guilford Press.

[19] American Psychiatric Association (1994). *Diagnostic and Statistical Manual of Mental Disorders*, 4th Edition. American Psychiatric Association: Washington, DC.

[20] Bulik, C.M., Sullivan, P.F., and Kendler, K.S. (2003). Genetic and environmental contributions to obesity and binge eating. *International Journal of Eating Disorders*, 33: 293–8.

[21] Gluck, M.E., Geliebter, A., Hung, J. and Yahav, E. (2004). Cortisol, hunger, and desire to binge eat following a cold stress test in obese women with binge eating disorder. *Psychosomatic Medicine* 66: 876–81.

[22] Geliebter, A., Ladell, T., Logan, M., Schneider, T., Sharafi, M. and Hirsch, J. (2006). Responsivity to food stimuli in obese and lean binge eaters using functional MRI. *Appetite* 46: 31–5.

[23] Grilo, C.M., and Masheb, R.M. (2000). Onset of dieting versus binge eating in outpatients with binge eating disorder. *International Journal of Obesity Related Metabolic Disorders* 24 (4): 404–9.

[24] Marcus, M.D., Moulton, M.M., & Greeno, C.G. (1995). Binge eating onset in obese patients with binge eating disorder. *Addict Behaviors*, 20 (6): 747–55.

[25] Spitzer, R.L., Yanovski, S., Wadden, T., Wing, R., Marcus, M.D., Stunkard, A., Devlin, M., Mitchell, J., Hasin, D. and Home, R.L. (1993). Binge eating disorder: Its further validation in a multisite study. *International Journal of Eating Disorders*, 13: 137–53.

[26] Dansky, B.S., Brewerton, T.D., O'Neil, P.M., and Kilpatrick, D.G. (1998). The nature and prevalence of binge eating disorder in a national sample of women. In Widiger, T.A., Frances, A.J., Pincus, H.A., *et al.* (eds), *DSM-IV Sourcebook*. Washington, DC: APA Press, Inc.

[27] O'Reardon, J.P, Ringel, B.L., Dinges, D., Allison, K.C., Rogers, N.L., Martino, N.S. and Stunkard, A.J. (2004). Circadian eating and sleeping patterns in the night eating syndrome. *Obesity Research*, 12 (11): 1789–1796.

[28] Gluck, M.E., Geliebter, A. and Satov, T. (2001). Night eating syndrome is associated with depression, low self-esteem, reduced daytime hunger, and less weight loss in obese outpatients. *Obesity Research* 9 (4): 264–7.

[29] Allison, K.C., Grilo, C.M., Masheb, R.M. and Stunkard, A.J. (2005). Binge eating disorder and night eating syndrome: A comparative study of disordered eating. *Journal of Consulting and Clinical Psychology* 73 (6): 1107–15.

Index